G000075333

Super Vixens' Dymaxion Lounge

Hillary Johnson is a contributing editor at L.A.'s *Buzz* magazine, and the author of two novels. She has lived in France and India, and for the past five years she has made her home in Los Angeles, where she lives with her son Tyrone.

★

Super Vixens' Dymaxion Lounge

Hillary Johnson

INDIGO

First published in the USA 1997
as A Buzz Book for St Martin's Press

First published in Great Britain 1998
as an Indigo paperback original
Indigo is an imprint of the Cassell Group
Wellington House, 125 Strand, London WC2R 0BB

Copyright © 1997 by Hillary Johnson

The right of Hillary Johnson to be identified as author
of this work has been asserted by her in accordance with
the Copyright, Designs and Patents Act, 1988.

A catalogue record for this book is
available from the British Library.

ISBN 0 575 40159 1

Printed and bound in Great Britain by
Guernsey Press Co. Ltd, Guernsey, Channel Isles

All rights reserved. No part of this publication may be
reproduced or transmitted in any form or by any means,
electronic or mechanical including photocopying,
recording or any information storage or retrieval system,
without prior permission in writing from the publishers.

This book is sold subject to the condition that it shall not,
by way of trade or otherwise, be lent, resold, hired out, or
otherwise circulated without the publisher's prior consent
in any form of binding or cover other than that in which it
is published and without a similar condition including this
condition being imposed on the subsequent purchaser.

99 98   10 9 8 7 6 5 4 3 2 1

Contents

''We ask ourselves, who am I
to be brilliant, gorgeous,
talented, and fabulous?''

—from Nelson Mandela's 1994 inaugural address
(posted in the waiting room of a Uruguayan
dentist's office on Sunset Boulevard)

Super

Vixens'

Dymaxion

Lounge

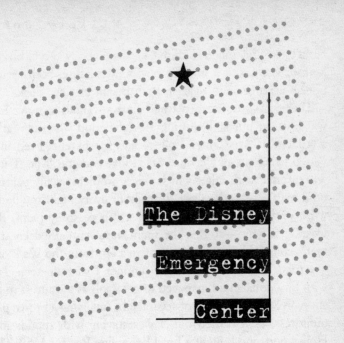

The Disney
Emergency
Center

★ I got knocked up the very day I arrived in Los Angeles, which was Cinco de Mayo, 1991.

There's a picture of me taken three days before I moved to Los Angeles, in front of my mom's apartment building in Portland, Oregon. I'm leaning on the hood of the white '68 Cadillac I'd bought for the drive to California. I'm wearing a Levi's jacket, my blond hair tied up in a red bandanna. The bandanna, the Cadillac, the Levi's, the blondness, all were reactions to the fact that I'd left my Indian husband six months earlier, trading West Bengal for New York. None of those all-American accoutrements had been needed or desired in Calcutta, where we'd spent the two years of our marriage. I looked unremarkable, less au courant than a Coke commercial, but because of my recent history, these stock iconographs felt deeply perverse. I may have looked like a cheerleader manqué, but in fact I was deeply exhausted and the reason I had picked L.A. as a destination was that it felt like the only place I

hadn't already ruined. I didn't know anybody there, but I had a
kind-of agent and a kind-of boyfriend waiting, both casual, hip-
pocket arrangements at best, both begun in New York.

There was a time when I had always wanted to move to L.A. I
was born in Burbank, during a brief period when my father was
a student at Art Center College and my parents lived in a con-
verted garage in an alley just off Hollywood and Vine. The garage
was infested with mice, which was a problem, as my parents slept
on a mattress on the floor. Just about every night my dad would
wind up attacking a mouse with a can of spray paint, the only
weapon at hand—so that the room was eventually decorated with
many colorful kill zones. This mere steps from the Walk of Fame.

I tried to move to L.A. the summer I was nineteen. I arrived
with fifty dollars and managed to get a job as a waitress in a coffee
shop on Sunset, the first of several jobs involving a brown polyester
minidress, as it turned out. I was staying with friends in North
Hollywood, and bought a Ford Econoline Van for $150. Then one
day a crazy Vietnam vet took my van apart in the coffee shop
parking lot, after which I could never get it to go over thirty miles
per hour. I gave up and went back to school.

The morning of May 5 I woke up in a Motel 6 in Bakersfield
and motored into town. When I hit the first L.A. suburbs, I pulled
into a gas station and changed into a flowered fifties dress that I'd
inherited from my grandmother's best friend, Laverne. Laverne
had been a career girl, an executive secretary who lived in an
apartment instead of a house, an apartment where the white satin
bedspread spilled onto white plush carpet. The dress was one
she'd bought on a business trip to Honolulu. I wore it for good
luck.

I drove to my kind-of boyfriend's house in Venice Beach, getting
there about one o'clock in the afternoon. He wasn't there, so I
took a walk on the boardwalk, in my fabulous fifties Hawaiian
frock. The sun was beautiful, I had aching style, and I'd just
stepped out of a '68 Caddy with an original push-button radio. I

didn't walk; I traipsed. After two years in India, swathed in khadi—that is, the fashion-free, government-sponsored cotton all my radical New Delhi friends wore—I felt like a sailor on leave, all cranked up with raunch and glee.

On the boardwalk, there were body builders who looked as if they had themselves steamed and laminated every morning. Couples in Gap khaki, their feet in clogs and their hair in ponytails, leaving the air perfumed with fabric softener as they passed. Latina girls with perfect lips and eyebrows, an Egyptian carriage of the head, their bodies all floppy from their baby-fat cleavage on down. The buff black guys who smelled like the inside of a new car.

Then I noticed that no one was looking back. This was strange! In India I'd been used to the freak-show stares of whole villages, or guys who threw rocks at you or tried to run you over with their Vespas because they thought you were cute. I'd even been chased through a Himalayan forest by a group of horny Sikhs. I'd found India to be a deeply asexual place, where arousal usually took the form of scorn and harassment. Since coming back, I'd learned to love the friendly catcalling I got in New York from the slick black guys and Italian shopkeepers—I always said thank you and blew them a kiss, even when construction workers made animal sounds and did funny things with their tongues. So why now zip, zilch?

Troubled, I bought a pair of four-dollar sunglasses with blood-red lenses from a street vendor, and sat down at a sidewalk café, ordering a cup of coffee and some French fries that appeared to have no grease in them at all. I hid behind my coffee and my glasses, watching the passersby as if they were Stepford People.

The red-lensed glasses made everything a vivid burnt yellow at first, but after a while my eyes adjusted, and I saw a new spectrum of colors, just like the old ones but vaguely artificial.

Right then I saw my first pair of silicone implants. They belonged to a tiny little sunbaked woman whose wiry, steroidal body precluded their being a natural occurrence. It was the first time I'd seen cleavage without a bra—or, indeed, a fat-free double-D. I like to remember her on roller skates. She couldn't have been five-two, even if she had on skates. Skin like a razor strap. Blond hair like straw, cut in a Rod Stewart shag.

Here was a healthy, plastic sense of self, sculptural and ana-poetic, conspicuously soulless, utterly corporeal yet without any trace of carnality. It seemed, I imagined, like the German nudist camps of the 1920s, aerobic and prefascist.

I was a visual dog whistle, simply outside the natives' range of perception. I flattered myself thinking that I could have been walking down the boardwalk arm in arm with Jane Russell and Betty Grable, and nothing would have happened. The sexual air on the beach was not about my kind of artifice at all, or any other kind. Artifice was something I wouldn't see again until I started running with drag queens—but that would be a few years later.

My kind-of boyfriend was home when I limped back, my dress wilted, my heel bleeding from the strap of my sandal. By now I knew it was Cinco de Mayo. None of the Mexican guys in their cars looked at me. As it turned out, my kind-of boyfriend wasn't all that happy to see me, either.

☆

The summer before my divorce I'd whiled away in the Himalayas, hanging out with a crew of river rafting guides. I'd wake with the sun and wave good-bye to "the guys" as they trudged off with their paddles and life vests. Then, like some wacko Julie Andrews, I'd take to the hills, tripping over mountain trails, scaling rocks, cavorting in the spray of hidden waterfalls, and basking on river-banks engrossed in a dog-eared copy of Conrad's *Heart of Dark-ness,* which was the only artifact of Western Civilization I'd brought with me. For lunch I'd have bread and oranges, and oc-casionally I'd share a cigarette with some ancient peasant woman with a bale of firewood on her back. In the evenings I'd come down and sit on the front porch, dandling the landlady's children on my knee while the servants cooked up the most wretched and pitiful vegetarian suppers known to man. Then the guys would come trudging home from a hard day's rafting—the guys, my buddies, my pals, a bunch of handsome, adventure-seeking lugs who told stories, played the guitar, and drank great quantities of Red Bull rum. They were wonderful, comradely fellows, and we all flirted like mad and never slept together. Oh, I was happy!

When the rainy season began, I came down from the mountains newly galvanized, made bold by happiness and ready to make sweeping changes in my life, which I did—and I haven't been happy since.

What followed were what I like to think of as the Dark Ages, times full of the melodrama of divorce and car accidents and back taxes. I moved to California and started life over from scratch, which was something I was really too old to be doing. Somehow it's fine to be driving around in an uninsured and unregistered Dodge Dart when you're in your twenties, but after thirty that kind of thing loses its renegade thrill. Until very recently, I lived in this state of necessary abjection, paying dues and waiting to get a life. Even though my brush with happiness was the thing that prompted me to embark on this miserable journey, I realize now that my goal was never to be happy, but to be authentic. I've been unhappy for years now, but at least I know that I'm finally in the right place at the right time.

Happiness has never been my strong suit. I grew up in the Pacific Northwest, where everything is moldy and damp and plaid. I took a few drugs in high school, but not all that many, probably because they were too much fun. This was the 1970s, long before grunge, though I can certainly attest that many a Northwestern youth before Nirvana and Pearl Jam lacked the will to bathe and the coin for a cup of espresso. No one I knew watched *The Brady Bunch*—these were the days before remote control, and watching television would have been far too much trouble for anyone I knew. We listened to Bessie Smith records, wrote fragments of bad poetry, and sometimes even went camping in the rain—but we were never, never happy.

It isn't clear to me in retrospect whether I wanted to be an artist because I was miserable, or vice versa, but I always knew, growing up, that I wanted to be Norman Mailer. Having barely survived a high school modeled after *Lord of the Flies,* I produced a facsimile of a novel, at nineteen, about death in the trenches in World War II. No cheerful coming-of-age stories were ever going to come out of *this* girl's battered Smith Corona.

When I moved to New York after college, I was thrilled to find myself ensconced in a veritable artist's garret, banging out bleak fiction in a weekly hotel full of vagrants and maniacs. I was in my element in New York, where a big, goofy grin and a dollar would get you a ride on the IRT—if nobody pushed you onto the tracks. There were times, walking through Central Park in the snow at noon with a hole in my shoe, when I felt a strange rising sensation in my chest, a levity born of my utter abjection. Ye joy-mongers take note: no amount of senseless euphoria can match the heavy, swollen, lush, fevered opulence of a moment of true *despair.*

Of course, it wasn't all bad. I read a lot of good books, I had friends, I even fell in love a couple of times, once with a grad student who explained that "love" is properly defined as "a state of enduring and diffuse solidarity," right before he broke my heart by running away with a Marxist feminist anthropologist. Even heartbreak was precious then, as I spent more and more time alone in my room, feverishly scribbling. But eventually the core of my being was consumed by failure, and my cursed inability to get a single word into print. Norman Mailer, I felt certain, hadn't spent his twenties temping for an ad agency.

Years passed before I got that longed-for bolt from the blue, a phone call from an editor who wanted to publish one of my novels. I remember distinctly the physical sensations that accompanied the news: my lungs collapsed, all feeling went out of my extremities,

the inside of my skull itched, and I wanted to throw up. All I
could think was *Aneurysm*.

It would seem that getting a novel published should have made
an impression on me, but by that time I'd reached a state of ir-
reparable neurasthenia brought about by typing too much ad copy
under fluorescent lights, I hadn't written a word in a couple of
years, and I had an Indian fiancé who was already picking out
curtains.

I failed to wake up from this desultory stupor, and the punishment for my misstep was two years in Calcutta, unhappily married
to a very nice man. I had great plans to make like Günter Grass
abroad and pen one grim, reflective masterpiece after another, but
it never happened. Instead I sank further and further into the
couch, reading Jane Austen and back issues of *The Economist*. I
was depressed. This would have been fine, except for one thing:
angst is unheard of in South Asia. Troubled Indians might develop
a tic or a twitch, or set themselves on fire over some fine point in
the government's educational policy, but rarely do they exhibit any
kind of *mood*. No, they leave the wallowing to the water buffalo.
I was, apparently, the only person in Calcutta with an affective
disorder. Talk about culture shock. How I missed the irony, the
disaffection of home!

But then came that heavenly Himalayan idyll, when I ran up
and down mountains like a maniac and realized, in doing so, that
such a thing as happiness was indeed possible. There I was at long
last, a living, breathing, functioning, integral being, full of vitality
and purpose. I felt fit and ready as never before. I didn't write a
novel that summer, but I felt as if I could have, if only I'd thought
to bring a pen.

So I got a divorce and came back for the pen.

☆

I had a vague idea I'd write screenplays, or magazine articles, or
whatever, just to make a buck. Meanwhile, I moved into a studio

apartment in Silverlake and started working as a temp at the
Southern California Gas Company, which was downtown, in the
tallest building in Los Angeles. The other secretaries were quick
to tell me that the building was on "rollers" or "ball bearings" so
that we'd be safe in case of a quake. They always added, reassur-
ingly, that *the whole building moved all the time.* These girls
weren't like the secretaries from Queens, Catholic girls who got
lunch from Blimpie's and went on package vacations to singles
resorts in Jamaica and spent hours in the ladies' room dishing and
putting on eyeliner. If you were a temp, you got to be their little
sister, and they expected you to tell them all about the wild parties
you went to and the guys you fucked, and they would never let
the boss stick you with "busywork." The downtown L.A. secretaries had two-hour commutes to tract houses in the Valley, and
an unparalleled reverence for employment. They ate skinless
chicken and wore pantyhose and took aerobics classes on their
lunch hour and always wanted to know if you minded before they
asked you a personal question, like "Do you know how to do a
mail merge on Windows?" Not to mention the jobs in L.A. paid
a lot less.

Every morning I exited the elevator on the forty-second floor
of the gas company and walked past the receptionist and the enormous Ed Ruscha paintings behind her.

I sat in a beige cubicle all day every day. There was a phone on
the desk, and my job was to answer it. I was there for two weeks,
and the phone rang twice. I sat at my desk and cried all day every
day. After two weeks, I was sent to Warner Bros. in Burbank. At
Warner Bros. I was a secretary in the Airline Rights Acquisitions
department. The secretaries here wore jeans and had self-esteem.
But then, this was the Entertainment Industry. I sat at my desk
laughing and puking until I knew I was pregnant.

I lived in Silverlake for only six weeks. Shortly after we realized
I was pregnant, I moved in with the boyfriend, whose name was
Scott. The cottage in Venice was three blocks from the beach and
the boardwalk. It was cute and dirty, with permanently sandy

floors, one fair-sized room that served as living room and kitchen,
a bedroom the size of a bed, and a bath with a moldy shower stall.
We found a flamingo-pink vinyl sofa at the Salvation Army, and
painted the walls bright yellow, blue, and gray.

In Venice, I learned how to fight. I had been married to a guy
who made the Mahatma look like a drunken sailor. I had never
once heard him raise his voice in all the years I'd known him.
Scott, I soon found, was handy with a harsh word, and had a
particularly unfortunate personality quirk: the sight of another's
pain always made him angry.

I was in the habit of exhibiting much pain, on top of which
pregnancy made me sick and irrational. There were times in India
when strange varieties of dysentery had laid me out, vomiting and
hallucinating, but this was far worse.

I was like a chicken bomb. To make a chicken bomb, put a
chicken in a plastic bag, fill the bag with milk, seal it, and leave it
somewhere. After about a week, the chicken bomb explodes. You
can imagine.

His voice contemptuous and controlled, Scott drilled into me
for being fat and lazy, and I spat bile back. We hated each other.
Eight months pregnant and weighing 170 pounds, I was sobbing
and stabbing the kitchen table repeatedly with a butcher knife,
screaming "Shut up! Shut up!" while he enumerated my faults
over and over in a booming midwestern monotone. I splintered
door jambs. The whole nine months, my first in L.A., are a blur
of saliva and ginger ale mixed with tears, swollen eyes and ankles,
and lots of blinking into an unfamiliar sun. When the baby was
three weeks late, I seemed merely to have reached a permanent
equilibrium of fluid and wounded hostility.

The bright side was that the Latino boys on the boardwalk really
went for pregnant girls, and I found myself once again subject to
an admiring eye from time to time, or a sexy, chivalrous smile. I
took to wearing a lot of minidresses on my walks to the bookstore
and the vegetable stand.

Tyrone was born in February 1992 in Santa Monica, at the Disney Emergency Center. A few months later, Scott and I split up, though it was several months before either of us could afford to move out of the shack in Venice.

The day Scott left, I went to a party and picked up a guy. Under the ambient party lights, he looked like a shorter, blonder Keith Carradine; he said he was a painter. The next morning, the painter turned out to be a vegan astrologer with something like three percent body fat. He got up at six A.M.—to go jogging, he said. Sex with this creature was dry, odorless, flesh-free, disconcertingly clean. A ride through an automatic car wash with the windows open would have been wetter and nastier. I'd been married, and later boyfriended, for so long that this was really my first safe sex, too—I'd used condoms before, but this act seemed wildly prophylactic. I imagined being probed by an assiduously polite customs agent at the airport, or getting fucked in a toy store by G.I. Joe, his freshly de-cellophaned hair still smelling of polypropylene. I remember thinking: so this is sex in Southern California. It seemed right out of a J. G. Ballard novel, an alternate future unfolding in a topsy-turvy place where cars and shopping malls are the sexual prosthetics of choice, where the human body itself is but a purgative abstraction, brought under strict authoritarian control through a scientifically masterminded program of surgery, enemas, and gang violence.

After the astrologer/painter/jogger guy left, I had a Bromo-Seltzer and went back to bed. I lay there thinking about all my false starts, near misses, and retrenchments of the past year: the bad boyfriend, the new baby, the temp jobs, all of it a long prelude. I lay there thinking, *Now I get it*.

I had arrived.

☆ Through a series of accidents and misunderstandings, I ended up becoming a journalist. First, a magazine hired me to write a short story; then they asked me and my "dark sensibility" to write an article about S&M nightclubs. I did, and some time later someone at the magazine gave my name to an editor at the *Los Angeles Times*, who called me up and asked if I'd like to do a weekly feature for the "Life and Style" section on, of all things, nightclubs.

This was ludicrous for many reasons, the least of which was that I had a baby on my hands. First, I don't like nightclubs and never did: the woof-woof, flash-flash gives me a headache. Second, I don't dance, and third, I'm known among my friends as someone who hates music. That isn't quite true, as I don't think anyone actually hates music; it's just that when I was sixteen, I was listening to 78s on a crank-up Victrola, while my peers were listening to whatever people listened to then—you see, I hardly even know.

But I was broke and therefore decided that I would be a perfect nightclub critic, so long as I could turn up enough cocktail lounges and wagon-wheel-chandeliered hole-in-the-wall joints to keep me out of trouble.

My idea of a good bar is a place that serves beer and jug wine in juice glasses and has a pool table with no waiting, a microwave with a sign taped to the door that says "Meatballs, 10 for $1," and Otis Redding on the jukebox. When I was growing up, my best friend, Karen, lived half a block away from a club on Martin Luther King, Jr., Boulevard called Geneva's, where we used to go to get barbecue, and which was the first place I ever heard "Brick House." We weren't old enough to be there, but we were lipsticky preteens, and I was usually the only white person, and more often than not a couple of guys would flirt with us while we waited for our take-out. Since then, whenever I heard about a good bar, I went there hoping for Geneva's, but either I was too old or Geneva's really was the best bar in the Western world and it was a useless search.

Hollywood bars were particularly bad. The first one I went to, taken there by an acquaintance from New York—both of us new in town, with purses full of parking tickets—was the Coach 'n Horses on Sunset, because this was supposed to be a good bar. I didn't think so. Though it was dark and beery inside, there weren't any old people, which means a place isn't serious, it has no legs. The same held true for the Formosa, a West Hollywood Chinese restaurant that had the virtue of inedible egg rolls, but also a homogeneous population of rock-and-roll types who all looked as if they considered "Stairway to Heaven" an old standard.

I found a measure of solace at the Spotlight, where one of the regulars was an elderly transvestite in a wheelchair, and I didn't mind Bob's Frolic in a pinch, or Jumbo's Clown Room, which was a lineoleum strip bar in a minimall on Hollywood Boulevard where the girls looked very real and some of the patrons actually wore raincoats—but I didn't think any of these would do for my maiden *Times* assignment, since I really did want the job.

It dawned on me that L.A. was the first place I'd lived where I didn't know anyone who wasn't white, and I decided that was ridiculous and headed south to look for Geneva's, or something like it, or at least a place where even if everyone was twenty-three, they weren't all white.

I landed first in Liemert Park, at Fifth Street Dick's Coffee House, which wasn't a bar or a nightclub, but was still a joint. A tall, narrow space lined with counters and stools, a stairway in the back, marked by a sign that read: "Support jazz and jazz players. This is your music. Only you can let someone else own it." The stairs led up to a low-ceilinged loft the size of a small motel room, with a tiny stage and some folding chairs, and a jazz trio playing furious bebop. Of course, given my nature, I don't really like bebop, but neither do I disapprove of it, and most of the time I like other people who like bebop, so I was happy, and I went downstairs and sat drinking coffee, and fell into conversation with a middle-aged white woman and her black daughter, who was a public school teacher, and a friend of theirs, a gray-haired man in a mudcloth coat and kepi who kept an African arts shop around the corner on Degnan Boulevard. It was a highly miscible crowd, everyone talking about the African-American renaissance and the community, again and again in excited tones, because it was new and they were still surprised that it was happening. Later, I walked over to the World Stage, a little place that looked like a storefront church, except that again it was jazz, and not even coffee this time, just the folding chairs. I sat, watching people listen, and ended up fascinated by a thirty-year-old man in knickers, socks, a tweed jacket, and a porkpie hat, who stood in the doorway surveying the scene, not entering, but stopping in to check it out on his way from one thing to another: it was an iconic image, and ever after it's been this man who springs to mind when I hear about "South Central" on the news—not the gangstas, not the riots, but the dapper man in the doorway of the jazz club who was on his way somewhere.

I left at two A.M., which I knew by then was still considered early in the evening in Liemert Park, where the real jam sessions began as the musicians who were in town to play the jazz clubs in Hollywood and Beverly Hills started dribbling in after their paying gigs let out. This was the place to be at six of a Sunday morning, if you were going to be anywhere other than bed, which I never am.

Then, on another trip south, I finally found my Geneva's—a blues tavern called Babe and Ricky's Inn on Central Avenue and Fifty-fourth. It's a frankly scary neighborhood, and you park, I'd been told, where the doorman can see your car. The doorman was a small, scarred, near-hunchbacked, pop-eyed man in an old army jacket that hung to his knees.

Inside it was a shotgun tavern; like all such spaces, it had a bar along one wall, a stage opposite, and room to barely squeeze past the bar stools to the booths in the back. The pool table was covered with a board and a tablecloth, on it the remains of somebody's birthday cake. On stage, an old man in a Jheri Curl and a sharp three-piece pinstriped suit with a nipped-in waist and flared trousers was on the sax, backing a proud-chested singer in a double-breasted maroon gabardine with a luxe sheen to it. In the booth closest to the stage, an enormous woman was enthroned on a pair of big pillows, the kind you normally see on a bed. She wore a black sequined dress and a black sequined hat on her gray, very coiffed head, and her eyes and mouth seemed to have been frozen in a benign smile for centuries. She nodded to the music, and between songs nodded in something I interpreted as general approval of a world in perfect working order, at least in that barroom eternity of which she was clearly the mistress. I knew right away that she was either Babe, or Ricky, or Babe or Ricky's mom, and that she'd always sat in that booth, and would be sitting there for ever and ever, and I worshipped her.

My friends and I shared a booth with an elderly couple in evening wear, who were on the way to their son's birthday party. We asked for martinis, and the waitress shook her head and said,

"Beer." We said, "Okay, beer," and drank Budweisers from the bottle, while the couple next to us winked and doctored their Cokes from a half-pint of rum.

When the band took a break, an old guy in a cowboy hat approached the jukebox, then looked across the bar at the proprietress and called out, "Laura! Is it okay?" She nodded and waved a queenly hand at him, and he dropped his quarter in and played his song.

We weren't the only white people, or the only young people, or the most fabulous or pretty people, by far. On the way back from a trip to the rest room, I smiled at Laura, and she reached out and took my hand. "I hope you're having a nice time," she said, "thank you for coming." I felt like bawling, or like sliding into what was left of the booth next to her and sitting there for ever and ever. This was a perfect world, and even though I was a visitor, I felt more at home than I did in any of the places I really lived. I must have been romanticizing the situation—but then, that's ultimately what the nighttime congress of strangers in a bar is for: being an outsider in a warm room. Who doesn't feel at home in the act of tearing shreds of romance from the teeth of pain, listening to someone with a life sing the blues? That is what a good bar is all about, and that is how I felt at Babe and Ricky's.

I wrote up Liemert Park for the *Times* story (I couldn't write about Babe and Ricky's, it was too personal), and I got the job. After that I covered Russian cabarets in the Valley, piano bars in Santa Monica, even the cocktail lounge in a Denny's restaurant in Glendale, anyplace where I wouldn't have to dance and that wasn't too noisy, and I went back to Babe and Ricky's a couple of times before it closed down for good, though not as often as I might have since I had to go to so many new places for my new job.

Then I learned that I was in fact, technically speaking, a "society writer" for the *Times,* and that my job also included something called party coverage, which meant that I ended up one night stuffed into a three-dollar ball gown from Goodwill, playing patty-cake with Bob Hope at a reception for Prince Andrew at the Beverly Wilshire Hotel, which was both exciting and humiliating, and I realized with a shock that I was now a journalist.

⭐ Cocktails at the Playboy Mansion, poolside.

A tall, gray-haired gent in a white *Saturday Night Fever* suit is dancing wildly, while a plump, ethereal blond girl in a floaty costume stands by in an attitude of beatific servitude.

"Who are you?" I ask. I'm a journalist, so I get to do this.

"My name is Kaytoo," the man says. "That's K-2, like the mountain. We are involved in a quest to make it possible for mankind to live up to its full potential, which we regard as a transmutation in a psycho-neurophysiological sense. A mutation in the brain cells! The human being doesn't live long enough to mature!"

I compliment him on his shirt.

He gestures to the floaty acolyte, who slips her arm coyly through his and smiles into space. "She made it," K-2 says. "She sat in a hammock in Cozumel for two hundred and fifty hours and made this shirt!"

I thank him for his time, and slip away. "The human brain is detrimental to life itself!" he shouts like a battle cry over the drumming disco.

A woman in a business suit accosts me, wearing a desperate look. She grabs my arm. "It goes against everything I believe in," she says with intensity, leaning in close, "but *where are the Bunnies?*"

I look at her with a fair imitation of sympathy. She's probably a D girl at a TV production company, or a studio publicist, or a story editor. The kind of woman who admires Jodie Foster, Susan Sarandon, and Emma Thompson, without ever considering that they all have great tits, power tits, tits like big hairy balls, the breasts of the justified. No, there are no Bunnies here tonight. Those days are gone. We don't need Bunnies anymore.

"Haven't you heard?" I say. "The cold war is over."

I leave her looking puzzled and abandon the cocktail crowd, wandering down past the koi pond, among the pink flamingoes, peacocks, mallards, and other gaudy birds resplendent in their mating plumage.

Excited whispers drift across the lawn:

"Have you seen the hot tub?"

"I hear there are monkeys down there."

"I saw penguins."

"Is this a Massengill commercial?"

"Is that Brad Pitt?"

The sound of visitors to a museum. I dub it the Titty Museum. *Here we have the ancient art of psychoanalysis, as practiced in a Herman Miller ponyskin lounge chair. . . . And here's the coke spoon Warren Beatty used in* Shampoo. *. . . And over here, we have the herpes virus . . . you remember the herpes virus?*

I wander farther down the hill behind the Mansion, where I can hear nothing but faint murmurs and the sound of ice tinkling in my glass. It seems loud, like the last thing you'd hear before the flash and the mushroom cloud and the big shock wave. This was wishful thinking, in a way, a kind of nostalgia for a time when nihilism was literal and the self was an enigmatic frontier, an era that peaked in 1967 with the sentimental hysteria of James Coburn in *The President's Analyst*. I've watched this movie four or five times in 1996. Hippies. Free love. The Russian spy with the heart of gold. The villain turns out to be the Phone Company, which is run by robots. . . . Oh, for the innocent paranoia of those Good Old Days!

The fifties. The sixties. The seventies. The eighties. The Titty Museum. It lasted until the Berlin Wall fell, at which point Hugh Hefner got married, had kids, and hung up his purple pajamas for good. Tonight he is in a suit, probably Armani, though I hope for the sake of historical integrity that it's a Pierre Cardin.

I make my way back to the pool. I need a loo, and find one in a pool cabana that looks like a seventies wine bar, the kind of place that was always called The Hobbit. There's a dimmer switch next to the commode, and a bowl of bobby pins next to the sink. On the way out I bump into a woman in a tuxedo. She has a cigar in one hand and a sushi roll in the other.

I spot Mel Tormé.

At the bar, I try to get a drink, but instead I end up in a pitch meeting with a loathsome, tubby creature who claims to be a movie producer. "It's a John Wayne, Tom Cruise kind of thing!" he exclaims. "A musical kickboxing thing!" As I turn to leave, he slips me his business card. "I went to college with Stallone," he whispers.

I lose him, because the fifty-four-year-old Nancy Sinatra is about to make her comeback by performing "These Boots Are Made for Walking" on a cramped little stage.

The whole evening seems less like nostalgia than like some kind of traumatic flashback. To be nostalgic, you have to actually miss something, and I don't think anyone actually misses Nancy Sinatra—or even, for that matter, the bunnies. What we're feeling instead is separation anxiety, a neurotic suckling whelp's attachment to the past. Yes, I'll be the first to say it: I miss the Soviet Union. I miss living in fear. I miss Freud. I miss tits.

Once upon a time there was the Evil Empire and the Playboy

Mansion. There was the objective end of the world on the one hand, and on the other, the seemingly limitless potential to discover an even better rack of goodies. It was the world according to Hef and James Bond. For 007, Saving the World was just an excuse for another titty safari, and there was no question that sex was on an existential par with nuclear Armageddon.

In the nineties, tits are no longer shaped like missiles, but melons. Like all domesticated wildlife, they are no longer angular, no longer dangerous, but round and tame. They stay corralled right where they belong, even without a bra. There is no longer any mystery, any lore, in the search for great tits. They're everywhere. There are no more titty safaris, no more narrative adventures around the search for the perfect nipple. How did this come to pass?

I remember when Mariel Hemingway got tits in order to win the role of slain centerfold Dorothy Stratten in *Star 80*. It was a darkly glamorous occasion, as I recall, like De Niro beefing up for *Raging Bull*. Her act, and the way she handled herself around the press, displayed true *cojones,* the kind of swaggering, sentimental narcissism that made twentieth-century America great. Hemingway, like her grandfather, belonged to a race of overachievers in the field of decadence; their saving grace was that they were entirely willing to put a gun in their mouths and pull the trigger should things come to such a pass.

You could say that Mariel's radically gauche and somewhat brave act did for sex what Papa Hemingway's career did for fiction: through no fault of their own, more harm than good. Culturally, there is almost no difference between a cut-rate mammoplasty clinic in Utah and an MFA writing program in Iowa. These two seemingly disparate institutions end up at exactly the same place in the end: the world is finally safe for democracy, and we all will have to live with the consequences.

Hef, I hear, has bought the grave site next to Marilyn Monroe's. And the Playboy Mansion is up for sale.

On the way out, I see a crowd and make my way toward it:

Nancy Sinatra. She's holding court, receiving journalists and well-wishers. When it's my turn, she smiles, glassy-eyed, and introduces the man at her elbow. "This is my doctor," she says. It's gothic. Her jerry-rigged face looks like the front end of a Buick. I imagine the good doctor shooting her full of Thorazine in one of the louche velour bedrooms of the mansion.

I have to get a quote, now that I'm face-to-face with her, so I ask Nancy what she thinks of her upcoming tour to promote the six-page spread of her naked in *Playboy*. She pauses. "It's going to be easy," she says at last, "because I won't have to do sound checks."

"These boobs were made for walking," someone behind me wisecracks. *Yes,* I hear Nancy thinking, *and one of these days these boobs are going to walk all over you.*

The party is over.

Sirens

Doll-like and Dangerous

My favorite shade of lipstick is a color called Silent Red. It's a liverish, bloody, voluptuous unction, heavy with complicated pigments; the saturated hues of love and anger mixed together in a neurotic, regal, murderous, transcendent red. Over the years I've had long auburn curls, Louise Brooks bobs, and platinum buzz cuts, but always the red lips.

I never wear eye shadow, or rouge. Sometime back in the early eighties I figured out that seven different shades of iridescent powder and gobs of Maybelline Great Lash made me look more like Baby Jane than David Bowie, and I stopped wearing makeup.

Then, a couple of years ago, something in me snapped. I quite unexpectedly found myself over thirty, with a small child, a Volkswagen, a flat chest, and a blunt cut, living in Southern California. All quite by accident. One day I put on my favorite lipstick and saw a great, grinning baboon's bottom in the middle of my wan, weak-eyed face. I wiped it off with a Kleenex and threw the little ribbed gold tube in a drawer. I shuddered. Somehow, my former slutty, girlish disarray had undergone a subtle change; I had now become the perfect simulacrum of a posthippie hausfrau. I began to have nightmares in which I was always just about to sprout great, knuckly Hobbit feet and go Birkenstock.

The answer to my feminine identity crisis came one day when I was visiting Nancy (a good, game girl from Brooklyn Heights who looks on makeup with withering disdain, even though I know for a fact she goes to Beverly Hills once a month to be waxed from the waist down). Nancy's five-year-old daughter had been given a pair of false eyelashes in her Christmas stocking, a demure pair of black Ardell Sweeties. On the pretext of playing dress-up, I plastered them on, and suddenly there I was: the new me, vixen extraordinaire.

I didn't look made-up in the usual sense, but my face was brighter, my gaze more voluptuous, my mien both doll-like and dangerous.

I winked, then tossed my head back and let loose a throaty, wicked laugh, sounding like a Raymond Chandler moll. Moments later I was peeling down Silverlake Boulevard, reveling in the feel of the Santa Ana winds streaking through my stolen lashes. The next day I bleached my hair platinum, and the Silent Red went back in my purse.

Putting On a Face

A few weeks later I was at a Spanish stucco house in the Fairfax district, talking to Sharon Stone's makeup artist, Trisha Sawyer, for a story about *Casino*. "When I was a kid, I used to go next door to Wilma Alcorn's house," Trisha was saying. "She'd sit me on the counter and I would watch while she put on her face."

Trisha led me downstairs to her garage, trailed by a black cat named Mascara. The dark garage was lined with shelves, and the shelves held row upon row of plastic storage boxes that contained all of Sharon Stone's past, present, and future faces. The place was gleefully eerie, a kind of pop pharaonic tomb, a glamour girl's Cave of Wonders, both altar and archive.

Trisha heaved open an enormous wooden crate on wheels, the kind of toolbox my ex-boyfriend used to hold everything necessary to build a small house. The box was full of false eyelashes. Trisha knew my weakness.

For the next hour, we talked underlashes and overlashes. Trisha showed me how to cut a pair in half and wear them on the outer lid "for the *I Dream of Jeannie* look" and how to pile on three pairs at once for the sixties showgirl thing. She showed me the subtle sleight of hand entailed by individual false eyebrow hairs, and the delights of gaudy glue-on eyeliner strips encrusted with rhinestones. Most important, I took away with me a kind of beauty queen's Grail: hand-tied silk false eyelashes, the Cadillac of all facial accessories. Trisha thought I might still be able to get them at Columbia Stage & Screen Cosmetics.

Sure enough, when I walked into the little Formica shop on the corner of Sunset and Gower in Hollywood, there they were behind the glass display, my Wunder Lashes, each pair nestled inside a heart-shaped plastic case that sits on cotton inside a silver foil box, whisper-light and thirty dollars a pair. They looked like something you'd find in a locket around the neck of some sad, longhaired poet.

The salesclerks were all busy, and I browsed while I waited; the shelves mostly held specimens of fake werewolf hair and bloody eyeballs mounted on springs.

"No, it's like this," a skinny, tobacco-voiced woman in a leather jacket was explaining to one of the salesclerks. "The glowing tip of a cigar is embedded in the flesh of his neck." She sounded exasperated.

I was rescued by Suzette, a salesgirl and part-time makeup artist with orangey foundation rubbed into her eruptile chin. Suzette's claim to fame, she told me, was having once worked on Rodney Dangerfield.

When I told her that I wanted the Wunder Lashes, she looked at me askance and insisted that first I needed to try out this new eyebrow "system." She held a plastic stencil to my forehead and painted on the brow, the way furniture stores paint the letters on a "Going Out of Business" sign. Then she demonstrated a foundation that would add "color" to my preternaturally olive complexion. "You should wear black mascara," she said. I said I preferred brown. For the sake of comparison, she did half my face with each product. I looked like I was going out of business. I looked like I'd had a stroke.

Gently, I insisted on seeing the Wunder Lashes. Bored, Suzette pulled out a set and threw them on the glass counter. "They're expensive," she said.

I told her I'd be cutting them in half, so they would really only be fifteen dollars a pair instead of thirty. She gave me a startled, keenly assessing look and then grew suddenly furtive and excited.

"I have something to show you," she said in a conspiratorial whisper, and disappeared into the back room. She came back with a dog-eared copy of *People* magazine from August 10, 1992. On the cover was a perfectly dreadful picture of Marilyn Monroe, looking overexposed and frowzy, if no less goddesslike.

"It's a terrible picture," Suzette owned, "but I saved it because, *look*—the photo is so bad that you can see exactly how her makeup is done! See? Marilyn wore the lashes just on the end— like you!" In Suzette's mind, I was already some kind of freak prophet. "And the brown liner—you're wearing brown liner. See, in the picture, it's not black Marilyn's wearing, it's *brown*." I examined the picture, and it was true.

I plunked down my thirty dollars in a daze and raced out into the Hollywood sun, forgetting all about my one freak eyebrow.

A Moment of Silence for Ava Gardner's Neck

I wore my new, glamorous look to a dinner party soon after, at the home of John Spath and Donald Rawley, or the Duke and Duchess of Spath, as they sometimes prefer to be known.

Their house in Sherman Oaks is a mirrored jewel box stuffed with paintings, étagères, exotic curios, and perfume bottles; if you lifted the roof off, a ballerina in a pink tutu would pop up and dance slowly around on point while *Swan Lake* tinkled like cut glass under the stars. I would never dream of showing up for cocktails or dinner at the Spath Manor without dyeing my shoes to match my purse.

John is a painter, and the house is full of his landscapes. Lately he's been painting these kind of twisted, gargoylish monkeys engaged in human leisure activities. John has silver hair and a silver mustache, and I always picture him in a silk smoking jacket and ascot, even though I can't honestly say whether or not I've ever seen him thus attired. Donald justly considers himself "one of the last great social queens," and usually receives at home in some kind of vaguely Moghulish tunic and a great deal of Important Jewelry.

At this particular dinner, I met two fabulous gentlemen who have been arbiters of style since the forties: Michael Woulfe, who costumed Ava Gardner, and Bob Sidney, who often choreographed Rita Hayworth.

I have a poster of Rita Hayworth at home in my bedroom. "There never was a woman like GILDA," it says, above a sultry, strapless Rita who is smoking a cigarette and looking as if she'd as soon grind that Pall Mall out on your shoe as blow you a kiss. John and I have sat together in the book-lined Spath study, in front of the VCR, taking turns murmuring, "Oh, Rita," with an indeterminate, elegiac despair.

Together the four gentlemen admired my lashes over a pitcher of martinis, and sighed. "There aren't any glamorous movie stars anymore," Bob said.

Michael nodded in agreement, looking at me with a pity that extended to my entire generation. "I bet you can't name one movie star with an ounce of style."

"Sharon Stone," I offered.

"Ah, yes," said Michael, his eyes glowing momentarily bright. Then he shook his head sadly as if to say, Doesn't the exception prove the rule. "But she's the only one."

Sidney reminisced of quiet, magical evenings with Rita at Aly Khan's Swiss chalet. Later, between the salad and the lamb, the conversation turned to Ava. "I remember one evening in front of a restaurant, when I saw her step out of a limousine," Woulfe said. "She was wearing an evening gown that bared her shoulders, and carrying her sandals in her hand. She slung them over her shoulder, then tipped her head back and laughed. I remember thinking at that moment, that was the most beautiful thing I'd ever seen." There was a universal intake of breath at the table, as all four men fell silent in rapt memory of Ava Gardner's neck.

Over coffee, Woulfe began to go into the years he spent as "the only man who spoke to Howard Hughes on the telephone every day." He outfitted the starlets Hughes was courting, squiring them on shopping sprees, tending to their attire and posture. "During one of these conversations, he asked where I sat in the limousine," Woulfe said. "I said that I generally sat in the back, with them. He asked me not to; I should sit up front with the driver, because that way, the young lady would not have to turn her head in order to converse with me. That turning of the head would stretch the skin of her neck, you see, and he didn't want that. We had to take routes that avoided crossing any railroad tracks, as the bouncing would also contribute to the deterioration of the skin."

The oblique and mysterious Hughes gesture struck me as weirdly intimate, less crazy than wistful. How anxiously, maniacally sentimental! One can cry outrage, I suppose, at women in their thirties getting face-lifts. In *Vogue,* I read that at least one plastic surgeon recommends liposuction in the early twenties for best results. Well, maybe he's right. And why not? Beauty should be unhealthy. It should be bad for you, and painful, and over-reaching, a kind of sick-sweet torture all around, a dizziness of greatness and humiliation.

Hasn't beauty always been the poetic brainchild of anxiety? Nothing has really changed, or at least not in Hollywood.

All cynicism is defeated in that cultivated, savored, well-wrought yet unexpected moment when the great, mythic beauty steps forward, a perfumed arabesque of careless, cared-for flesh, throws back her head, and laughs.

I Want to Be Evil

Eartha Kitt performed at the Cinegrill, in the lobby of the Roosevelt Hotel. The Cinegrill is a drab room with little sense of history or atmosphere, despite or because of being on Hollywood Boulevard just opposite Mann's Chinese Theatre, or despite or because of the little-known fact that Liberace's brother, George, was the house pianist in the fifties. That must have been while Eartha Kitt was in Europe. Now she was here, packing the house every night for weeks on end. She was sixty-seven, and a minx.

Though I was seated in the back of the room, I could make out her enormous Barbie Doll lashes just fine as she batted them up and down at a businessman in the front row.

"Aren't you the guy who went out for a pack of cigarettes and never came back?" she asked him in her dusky falsetto. The caterpillar lashes went up and down again slowly. "And what's that piece of green apple pie you've got with you now?" she hissed, catlike, pointing a long, red nail at his date.

Then she tossed her head and sang "Uska Dara" in Turkish, and then she sang my favorite song, "I Want to Be Evil," about a good girl who wants to go bad.

After the concert, I dodged around the autograph seekers and asked her publicist, a bearded man named Alan, if I might have a word with Ms. Kitt. A short while later I found myself upstairs in Eartha Kitt's suite, her poodles Mootsie and Abba nosing at my knees. It all happened very fast. Eartha was talking to her musicians in the hallway, and Alan took me aside by the elbow and said, "Listen, I think you're okay."

"Thank you," I said, happy to be vetted, thinking it must have been the Wunder Lashes.

"So this is what I'm going to do," Alan said, still whispering. "I'm going to let you unbutton Eartha."

It took me a moment to understand what he meant, but when I did, it had the same effect as if I'd just been offered the opportunity to personally rip a virgin's heart out on an altar. "Thank you," I said, so flattered and frightened I wanted to die, "thanks a lot."

When Eartha floated into the room, I noticed with a start that her makeup looked like a mask, as if, now that she was offstage, she wasn't quite wearing it anymore. It seemed to hover slightly above the surface, but maybe this was because she wore absolutely no expression whatsoever. Alan whispered in her ear, and she turned in the doorway, arms held slightly out, and presented her back. Alan waved me in. I stepped up, and saw that there were in fact a million little silk-covered buttons running from her neck to the small of her back. The office of unbuttoner was dignitary, but not symbolic. She couldn't have done it herself. I unlooped button after button, slowly exposing her taut spine, the heat of her skin collecting heavy in my fingers. It was a weird, erotic, and historic performance. When I finished, she sailed away without turning.

Moments later she reappeared in a bright caftan, her face again animated. She curled up among the cushions on the couch while the poodles jumped nervously around her periphery.

She laughed at me right away. Thirty-dollar lashes? Perish the thought! "I don't believe in paying a lot of money for eyelashes!"

she declared, amused at my folly. "I think it's terribly funny that
we're conned into all this nonsense. And mink eyelashes! Who the
hell is going to know they're mink?"

"Is there such a thing as mink lashes?" I asked, and she laughed.
"Sure!"

I asked what kind she wore, and she walked me over to the
kitchenette, where she kept her lashes in their pink plastic box,
right next to her rice cooker. They were the same old Ardell lashes
you get at Woolworth's, and I noted down the model number:
747 Longs.

It was after midnight, and Eartha was tired. She was in the habit
of getting up every morning at six-thirty and jogging through
Burton Chase Park with weights on her ankles. We chatted for a
moment or two about exercise, and health, and the rice cooker,
and she confessed that her favorite thing in the world was a garlic
sandwich. A garlic sandwich! After the unbuttoning, I felt twice
blessed.

As I stood dreamily to leave, Alan took me aside again. "You
know," he said, "if you're interested in eyelashes, I also represent
Carol Channing and Anita O'Day. Anita just had permanent
eyeliner tattooed on. She's in Palm Springs right now, recover-
ing."

Anita O'Day. I sighed at the thought of meeting such a de-
mented angel as she. After a lifetime of sex, drugs, and jazz, she's
finally gotten tired of putting on her eyeliner every day.

And Carol Channing? Alan told me her natural lashes all fell
out long ago, she had abused them so. Now she always wore false
ones.

I adore the ever-so-wanton diligence of these women, the dignity with which they turn their formidable countenances on the
world, lips and lashes heavy with war paint. It frightens some
people, the sarcophageal style of the old legends. No fresh-faced
starlet on her way up is ever going to be as beautiful as an eight-
hundred-year-old Anita O'Day, her freshly inked eyes all greasy
with Bacitracin and shaded against the brutal Palm Springs

glare. It's her luminous voice that sings, "Leave your worries on the doorstep, just direct your feet to the sunny side of the street." The way she sings it, the song isn't coy or cloying, it's a sweetly manic jag, a bright spring day that's ever so slightly narcotic.

Makes a girl want to be evil.

The Virgin of Hollywood

I like to think of Tori Spelling as the secret daughter I never had, my Hollywood love child. She is my fantasy little girl, my fairy princess, the stuff of dreams and tawdry, sentimental illusions. I call her the Virgin of Hollywood, and I hold her to be the blond avatar of Our Lady of Guadalupe, the goddess Mexican *brujas* call Little Mother or Little Goddess, and who is said to be a Catholicized Aztec goddess Tonantzin. The Virgin of Guadalupe has many guises, and you can buy candles to burn to these diminutive girl-gods at every local supermarket. There for ninety-nine cents is Guadalupe as La Purisima, dressed in white, the Virgin presiding over money, herbs, and hair growth. When Guadalupe appears in robes of cerulean velvet, she is called Nuestra Señora del Asunción and helps in the entertaining of "higher thoughts" to help one rise above adversity. As Nuestra Señora del Nombre, in plain robes, Guadalupe offers improved memory and practicality. With a garland in her hair and rich robes, she is Nuestra

Señora del Rosario, patroness of art, music, and a good singing voice. In purple robes and a gold crown, she is La Reina, ruling over wit, eloquence, and fine speech. Dressed in austere robes, as Nuestra Señora de la Presentación en el Templo, she represents secrecy and privacy. It is striking how little difference there is between the idylls and idols of Hollywood and the slaughtered dreams of the Aztec nation. I wonder what kind of hieroglyphs will be made of the walls of the Spelling mansion many eons hence, and who will be worshipping, even as I do, at Tori's blond altar.

Sometimes I like to picture Tori in a baby-doll nightie, drifting on a sea of stuffed animals, all of which wear little floral-print animal clothes that match her California King bedspread.

Then there's my other Tori, kind of a Patty Duke identical-cousin thing, the Tori I imagine freebasing in the back seat of a Dodge Viper, or doing the nasty on Daddy's billiards table with some faceless cast member of the Mighty Morphin Power Rangers.

My most touching, painful, and beloved Tori is a kind of Carrie Fisher manquée, writing poetry in her rococo bathroom with a dog-eared copy of Bataille's *Story of the Eye* and a carton of hard-boiled eggs handy by the commode.

Tori is so utterly—*imaginable*.

As Raymond Chandler said, there are blondes, and then there are blondes. While everyone else is hunkered down over *Melrose Place,* I'm drawn over and over again to the afternoon reruns of *Beverly Hills 90210.* For me, Heather Locklear evokes nothing of the bombshell. Heather's just another grown-up mall rat! A rocker chick turned career girl, a nominal puppy-dog girl, boringly hard-bitten underneath that shaggy trademark 'do and those big shoulder pads. Tori, on the other hand, is another order of blonde, the good kind, so vulnerable as to be egoless. Nothing bad can ever happen to Tori. No amount of surgery-gone-wrong can mar her dear, droll, Mr. Potato Head looks. Beneath the ungainly peroxide helmet, the sleek, store-bought tan, and the short, trendy-girl frocks, lies a blind, oceanic state of being, all hope and hurt, the very essence of *girl.*

☆

I met my son's father when we wrote a screenplay together. I wrote
another screenplay when Tyrone was three months old, swinging
him with my foot while I typed on the computer.

Meanwhile, Tyrone's dad went out and took the Robert McKee
Story Structure Seminar. It's like EST: you sit in a convention
facility and are bombarded by hours of motivational jargon and
promises of wild success. I was horrified at the time, but I have
to admit in retrospect that for being a weekend crash course, the
McKee seminar did a pretty good job of disabling most of Scott's
quirky, instinctual artistic habits and replacing them with formulas
and catchphrases. The blockbuster script remained elusive, but
Scott became very good at keeping his son in line, fed, washed,
and in bed by nine, while my own lack of story structure meant I
still had peanut butter sandwiches in my file drawers and never
got Tyrone to bed before eleven.

I went out on pitch meetings for bad cable-TV erotica shows
and dallied with "producers" long before I knew that the idle rich
young of minor movie stars are commonly referred to as producers. *I have a fantastic story, and you're the one to write it!* Boys
with wan, blow-dryer hair and ill-fitting khakis, living in that more
and more familiar wealthy squalor of the Spanish-style stucco
house with the pool and the ugly antique rugs and country pine
furniture and the anodized black halogen lamp left over from the
all-black boy-decor of college days. All of it anxiously presexual.
They invite you over for endless breakfast meetings. *I tell you
what, I'll give you five hundred dollars to write a treatment.* The
cappuccino machine makes a sterile sucking sound in the kitchen.

I'd get home, dry-humped half to death, and proceed to slog
and bark my way through the evening: as a mother, I was a hack.
At this rate, my child would turn out as lame as any episode on
late-night cable, an appalling exercise in wounded mediocrity.

If only I were more like Candy and Aaron. Why couldn't I have
a child who sprang whole from my creative imagination like
Athena from the head of Zeus?

I started to have dreams, always the same: I'm being chased through the Spelling mansion by a bunch of preadolescent Amway salesmen. Tori is there, wearing pink Dr. Dentons with feet in them and sucking her thumb. She seems catatonic, shuffling through the mansion's marble halls.

Suddenly Aaron and Candy are there, at the door to a giant ballroom full of metal folding chairs. Candy tells me I am enrolled in something at the Learning Annex called the Robert McKee Parenting Seminar, and that it will cost me five hundred dollars. Amazingly enough, I have exactly five hundred dollars!

I take a seat. At first I'm a little bit disappointed to see that most of the people here are wanna-bes like me, then I spy a couple at the far end who look a lot like Warren and Annette.

"Conflict! Conflict! Conflict!" the seminar leader exclaims, sketching an angry diagram on the chalkboard. The circles he draws at the bottom are kids, with good and bad qualities radiating out of them in little spokes. They look like the suns my little boy draws all over my phone bill.

The parent to my left is a scruffy-looking, Altmanesque soul in granny glasses and Gap khakis, a burnt-out case if ever there was one. "Hi," I say, "great seminar, huh?" He smirks and says, "First time, eh?" I nod politely. "So you've been here before?" He coughs and beckons me closer with a crooked, dirty finger. I lean in close to listen, after glancing over my shoulder to make sure there aren't any Players watching us.

"What is it about children that gnaws away at the creative imagination?" he asks in a broken, delirious tone. "Why is being a parent so draining and monotonous and seemingly futile, a rote recitation of rules and traditions that one is always a little too tired and frustrated to rise above? You start out thinking you're going to do something special, something fine, but in the end it's just get it done, get through it, and move on."

I shudder and look away. But as the seminar drags on, I realize that this is never going to work. As a parent, I don't know a "Crisis" from an "Inciting Incident," I have no "Moral Vision,"

and I'm utterly incapable of "Establishing a Consistent Reality."
During a heated debate between two West Siders as to whether
or not toilet training can be considered a subplot, I sit bolt upright
in a cold sweat, screaming "Rosebud! Rosebud!"

Oh, how glad I was to wake up back in the hardscrabble reality
of my life, which is more like a tedious Philip Glass opera than a
Hollywood blockbuster. I wish Aaron and Candy all the best,
(hey—Tori is now the only virgin on *90210,* so don't try to tell
me they're bad parents), but I will never be a Hollywood mom,
nor do I any longer want to be one. I've learned my lesson, and I
can also thank my quirky, astructural Tyrone for inadvertently putting an end to my other Hollywood career.

The next time some fetus-faced producer or other called me up
saying that somebody or other had said I was a terrific writer, etc.,
etc., I promptly took off to Kinko's with two screenplays to be
copied. Then something happened: I never went back to pick them
up. Now, every few months, I get a message from a guy named
Tony asking am I ever coming to pick up these *screenplays.* Last
month the message was slightly more urgent: "Are you ever coming to pick up these, er, *original screenplays?*"

Well, it's been two years now, and I guess the answer is no.

I no longer go to pitch meetings; instead I write magazine articles about things like moisturizer and child care. I even interview
starlets for *In Style,* so I now know that all girls in Hollywood have
overstuffed sofas from Shabby Chic just like Tori's. It's a living on
the fringes, which seems to be where I belong. The screenplays I
lay at the feet of the Virgin of Hollywood, long may she shine.

Biosphere III

✩ Two A.M., Koreatown. Helicopters and searchlights actually wake me up. Usually I sleep through gunfire. This time I did, too, but the search is noisy and centered on my street. Out my living room window, I can see the searchlight scanning my driveway and the parking lot behind my apartment building; then moving next door through the playground of the Korean preschool and over the rooftop of the minimall where we get our liquor and pizza; then traveling across the street to the rooftop of the Koreana department store, which isn't really a department store but some kind of gambling parlor.

The helicopters isolate something or someone on the ground a block away. They hover there for a long time, making the neighborhood as bright as a supermarket.

A couple of months after I moved in, I drove up to find a TV news van pulling away from the curb while the guy from the pizza place hosed a puddle of blood off the driveway. Someone had just

been shot, he said. He didn't know who, or why. Had I come
home five minutes later, I would never have known about the
shooting. This incident became emblematic of that Koreatown
apartment: I didn't ever feel like I knew what was going on there,
or why.

When I first looked at the apartment, there was a family living
there, and the place smelled like boiling meat. I took it because it
was huge and cheap, and I'd just gotten seven thousand dollars as
a settlement from a car accident. The apartment had three bedrooms and a hallway the length of a regulation bowling alley. It
wasn't until I moved in that I noticed it had all been painted in
semigloss enamel, so it had a vibe like a Victorian mental hospital,
all shoddy and institutionally grand. Everything that happened in
the building's stairwell sounded as if it was happening in my living
room, so there was a constant breaking-and-entering sound track
at night. The toilets were the kind you flush with your foot. There
was even a full-sized fire hose coiled up in a corner like a Claes
Oldenburg sculpture.

I made the mistake, on moving in, of trying to pretty up the
dump with a coat of warm-colored paint, but it was the kind of
place where every aesthetic effort just underlines the general hope-
lessness of the situation. None of the windows closed, which was
all right since they were crusted in so many years' worth of dirt
you couldn't see out of them. There were holes in the backs of
closets that seemed to lead to the bowels of the earth. The kitchen
counters had been *painted*. The refrigerator had been *flocked*. The
scarred linoleum on the bathroom floor didn't even go all the way
to the walls.

My downstairs neighbors lived in an apartment of identical size
and shape that had been geegawed out of sight with knotty-pine
walls, tomato Formica, a faux-stone fireplace spread across one
vast wall, weird carpet, linoleum, and velvet sectional sofas snaking
all over the place, making pathways between half a dozen TV sets.
It was like a coral reef down there. The windows all looked out
on the concrete rear wall of the minimall. You walked in, and

you were underwater, in some amniotic America as elemental as it is inconceivable. The husband was a teacher, the wife a nurse, and they had a six-year-old boy named Darius. For some reason, I thought about their apartment all the time. It was like a parallel universe, one that was safe and warm, whereas mine was cold and windy and open to interrogation from the sky.

One day I was lying in bed with chicken pox, watching *Cops,* when suddenly there on the screen was my apartment building, as the LAPD brought a suspect to the ground in front of the Korean bridal shop across the street.

☆

I was single. Tyrone was two. I was living in Koreatown, doing odd magazine features, and I was poor. Then I was writing a column about babies and doing nightclub reviews for the *L.A. Times,* and I was slightly less poor.

For the first time in many months, I could afford to pay my car insurance premium on time. I would have, too, except for one insurmountable problem: I didn't have a postage stamp. The post office was only three blocks away, but according to my child-sized map of the universe, I might as well have trudged on over the hill to Sherman Oaks barefoot with a sack of pennies on my back to pay the damned thing in person.

When Tyrone was a baby, such raids on public services could be organized with little more than a day's notice. All that was required was a rucksack of gadgetry, fair transport, and a good night's sleep. Anything seemed possible back in those days: the post office, the copy shop, Radio Shack—why, we even went to the mall once. Then one fine day Tyrone grew out of his stroller. I was proud, sure, but the thing is, two-year-olds don't walk the way we do. Like us, they are oriented along a vertical axis, and like us, they are capable of both forward and backward movement at varying speeds, but *they don't go anywhere!* Occasionally one of them may appear briefly to be heading purposefully in a direction, but that's almost as rare as a chimpanzee typing Shakespeare.

The net effect was that the neighborhood post office was now three hundred and fifty miles away. Since Tyrone had jettisoned his diapers along with the stroller, that was way beyond our range. I could take the car, sure, but it's six miles of rough terrain to get to the driveway.

I tried once. Actually, our destination wasn't a post office, but a Payless shoe store. One thing about all this random oscillation— it's hell on tennis shoes. Tyrone was going through a pair a month. So there I was, juggling seven shoe boxes and chasing Tyrone up and down the aisles. You've seen Payless shoe stores on CNN: they're the ones that were universally looted during the riots; it was electronics, food, and Payless shoes. This is understandable. If I could build a nuclear weapon in my kitchen, I'd test it in a Payless shoe store. The place was full of fun-house mirrors and TV sets playing cartoons: very kid-friendly, I supposed—wrongly. As I knelt and fumbled shoes on and off quickly, while Tyrone was briefly transfixed by Batman, a high, whiny voice pierced the din. "Look at this mess! Look what you've done!" I looked up to see a horrid little cretin standing over me, feet planted wide, arms folded across his chest, exuding the kind of fearsome absolute authority shoe-store managers and postal workers are notorious for. "I want you to put them all back in the boxes and put them in the right places." "Y-yes," I stammered humbly, "just as soon as we're finished." "No, *now!*" the fierce little goblin intoned. Suddenly I'm Ned Beatty in *Deliverance,* crawling on hands and knees, trying to oink like a pig, some anonymous, all-powerful hick standing over me.

Shaken, I went home, locked the door, and set about conceiving a plan whereby I would not have to leave the safety of my own home again until Tyrone was fully grown. The apartment was big enough; between mail order and modems, we could create our own self-sufficient Biosphere.

One more venture *out there* was all it took: I went to the Salvation Army and bought an exercise bike, then swung by the local Korean minimall and plunked down $36.95 for a fax/modem. After that, a quick stop at Ralph's for frozen food, and we were off on our adventure.

DAY ONE: Tyrone is running around naked. I'm wearing a fluffy negligee, since the world as I know it has come to an end and I can wear whatever I want. I spend the day installing the fax/modem, while Tyrone pops the bubbles in the bubble wrap and throws all his toys out the windows onto the neighbors' cars. We have frozen Penne with Marinara and Italian Sausage for dinner.

DAY TWO: Tyrone agrees to let me use the exercise bike, as long as he gets to pedal. He's also decided to edit my AUTOEXEC.BAT file so that red warning signs flash on my screen when I try to play video poker with myself. Then he rubs tuna salad along all the windowsills, I imagine as part of some kind of baby-voodoo ritual.

DAY THREE: I discover Cyberspace! A whole universe of people who are old enough to type. I send E-mail to my friend Gina in Hawaii, and chat convivially on-line with people who have no idea what fetid squalor lurks behind the eloquent typing of this onetime data-entry clerk. We eat Linguine with Four Cheeses.

DAY FOUR: Tyrone finds a Magic Marker under the sofa and turns himself into a Keith Haring baby. I get a strange, misguided impulse to go to the post office, just for the company. Who knows, maybe they'd give me a job.

DAY FIVE: Garbage day, the urban single mother's nightmare. I slip into something a little less Miss Havisham, like shorts and a T-shirt, then gingerly heave a bag of week-old diapers (he still wears them at night) over my shoulder. Tyrone is jealous of his waste: he wants to be carried, too—down two flights of stairs, *around* the building, then back, dragging the trash can a hundred yards to the curb. When I put him down *just for a second* to unlock the gate, my little illustrated man runs into the road, growling and spitting. I save him, but not before he frightens the armed security guard at the Koreana department store. The last person to do that got shot, as I recall.

DAY SIX: The phone rings. I don't answer it. Why bother? I E-mail NASA to tell them that I'm qualified to spend long periods of time in a state of confinement and need a job. I'm willing to travel, especially at the speed of light, if that means Tyrone won't be two anymore when I get home from work. NASA doesn't answer.

DAY SEVEN: I realize I haven't clipped the family fingernails for a long time, but for some strange reason I decide not to. . . .

☆

That was before preschool (what a haunting phrase, "Before Preschool"—it sounds like the title of an Arthur Miller play). I was more or less housebound with two-year-old Tyrone, plotting various delusional scenarios involving foster homes and the Fiji Islands. In order to get him into preschool, I had to earn more money, but to earn more money I had to work more, which meant I had to get him into preschool. In fact, the system was breaking down, slowly but surely, as I lost my car insurance, my health insurance, my designer antidepressants, and occasionally my phone service, for lack of cash flow.

But it wasn't just the money thing. One desperate morning, after Tyrone woke me at six by pouring powdered ginger and seaweed all over my bed after I'd stayed up until four to finish an article that was already overdue, I called his father. "Come . . . take . . . the . . . child," I choked out. He said he couldn't leave work.

So I called my own father up in Oregon, who is always a good man in a crisis, averaging almost as many of them per annum as I do. "Come take the child," I said in Gregorian tones. He also couldn't leave work, but what he could do was send me a check to cover the first month of preschool.

I dragged Tyrone out the door, marched him down the block, and pounded on the door of the nearest Montessori school. The director, a Filipino woman, gave us the grand tour. "The playground's in the backyard," she pointed out. "Very safe from drive-by shootings." This struck me as one of the least reassuring remarks I'd ever heard.

I went to the local YMCA, where Tyrone has been on the wait-

ing list since November. The silver-haired directress said she'd
make room. The teacher was great, and our neighbor's daughter,
Nora, a sprightly, witty little number with a gift for mimicking all
states of humor with her big eyes, was a distinguished alumna. But
four hundred dollars a month for *part-time?* Sensing my hesitation,
the old bat who ran the place started rattling off the names of her
students' minor-celebrity parents. In a town where every shoe re-
pair shop has a wall of signed eight-by-ten glossies, even the
YMCA is a nickel-and-dime pantheon. I couldn't do it.

Next I looked at a school in an even worse neighborhood than
mine. It was extravagantly named after an Ivy League university,
and run by a dotty old Englishwoman I quite liked. But the
blighted playground looked ripe for a Samuel Beckett scenario,
and inside the ramshackle classrooms, everyone seemed to be re-
covering from a long-ago trauma, or else they were just beginning
to feel the effects of some slow-acting poison. The dolls all had
black scuff marks on their faces and were missing hanks of hair.
The somnambulant teacher put a record on a scratchy phonograph
and the kids played ring around the rosy: "Ashes, ashes, we all
fall down!" The game seemed too prophetic under the circumstances.

I narrowed the search down to two possibilities: the Christian
school and the Islamic school.

The Christian school was inexpensive, friendly, multi-ethnic,
and, being in a church, had great architecture. We were given the
grand tour—the playground, the kitchen, the gymnasium, the
classrooms, all splendid, spectacular, glowing with that pure, por-
celain warmth peculiar to Christians. And he could start on Mon-
day. I got a wonderful, creepy, tingling *this-is-it* feeling. We met
the teacher, who was obese and wall-eyed. Tyrone joined the class
as they sat down to read a story. A little boy came and sat next
to him, ready to make friends. "Settle down, Henry," the teacher
said, "or you'll have to stand in the corner!"

I'd like to say that I didn't wait to see the dunce cap, but hustled
my baby on out of there; in fact, I denied the whole thing, such

was my desperation. Now I understand those people who claim that they participated in satanic rituals with their entire families and then repressed the incident in the station wagon on the way home. I was ready to enroll Tyrone the very next day, but felt I should check out the last place on the list just for good measure.

The moment I entered the Islamic Center preschool my heart said *Inshallah!* The playground was bright and clean. So were the kids. The teachers reminded me of my ex-mother-in-law. I choked back tears, suddenly awash in sentimental reminiscence over the way she used to paddle about the house in her petticoats, a towel draped over her chest for modesty, admonishing servants and grown-up children in shrill Urdu and pidgin Bengali. This daily performance wasn't the least bit neurotic—no, it was Wagnerian. I don't care what anyone says, there's nothing on earth like an Indian mother for filial love, or gratuitous melodrama. Standing there in the bright, primary-colored preschool, I realized I wanted a little melodrama in my life. Sometimes a girl gets all alienated and self-actualized, here in the touchy-feely state of California. I liked it here among the Orientals, where there was not a speck of dirt of anomie, just softness and light and the scent of jasmine perfume mixed with cardamom.

And that's why Tyrone bows to Mecca every night before tucking into his Korean pizza. His friends are named Hakim and Gibran and Tanou. Instead of Power Rangers they play Sword of Allah on the playground. And in the Thanksgiving pageant this year, I sat among the ladies from Egypt and Pakistan in their chadors and Hermès head scarves, and the fathers from South Central in their mudcloth toques, applauding Tyrone's debut as a carrot in the school play, where he happily warbled out a rousing chorus of "Abu Youssef had a farm, eeeyi eeyi oh!"

Disaster

Relief

Scott and I barely saw each other once we split up. We'd both moved, and he'd never even seen the inside of my new apartment, preferring to wait at the curb when he came to collect Tyrone. Then after a while, our phone conversations began to include trivia about mutual acquaintances and ball games, and soon we were on friendly terms again. My memory has it that the only thing preventing this friendliness had been his hatred of me, but I think it's more accurate to say that I hated him in occasional, fierce bursts, while his hatred burned at a steady, low level all the time.

Then one day in June, Scott up and invited me over for Sunday dinner. It was a casual invitation, suggested as an adjunct to my picking Tyrone up, and I said sure, why not.

Scott was living in a two-bedroom ground-floor apartment two doors off Hollywood Boulevard near Western Avenue. He had installed a floodlight on his front porch to keep crack smokers

from sitting on his front steps (they moved to the back steps), and
his neighbors in the apartment next door were three guys who
worked at three different porn shops in the neighborhood. Across
the street was a motel with bars on the windows and a pool flush
with the street that no one ever used, probably because it would
have been like swimming in a storm drain—not that the motel
ever had a guest to begin with. Scott's landlady was a crazy bitch
who owned the Mongolian barbecue on the corner and had in-
explicable purple hair. The apartment was fine on the inside, but
it was not the kind of place you moved into unless you were se-
verely depressed. It was like the awful boyfriend or girlfriend you
have on the rebound, and it gave him more grief than I ever had,
with the addicts and the landlady and the shopping-mall construction out the bedroom window.

When I came for dinner, bringing wine, the first thing that
struck me was how much like our old place it looked. All our old
furniture was there—the flamingo vinyl couch, the lamps, the dining table made from a drafting board, the chests of drawers, the
plates, the silverware. And the artwork: Scott's life-sized nude self-
portrait, the wall-sized picture of a fat dictator clutching two missiles, the Jenny Holtzers, insane ravings in hand-set type on squares
of colored paper. Scott had painted the place in the same saturated, layered colors, everything ragged and sponged and brush-
stroked. Being in this apartment made me feel strangely
embarrassed; it was like having an awkward conversation with
someone you have no feeling for, but who still loves you. I knew
Scott didn't still love me, but I was rattled to see how little of our
life he had in fact rejected.

I had painted my new place in the flattest, beigest hue I could
find after living in those small, ratty, overpigmented rooms in Venice, but then I'm superstitious that way: if I've had an incredibly
awful experience, I always throw away the clothes I was wearing
when it happened. (Although there are some clothes that seem to
bring disaster, like the green lace Marilyn Monroe dress I had as
a teenager, that I keep stubbornly wearing because I love them,

despite bad dates, breakups, and ruined birthdays.) This lousy paint seemed like that to me, like it would never be a good thing to have around, no matter what, no matter how much money you had or how perfect the girl was.

Still, I complimented Scott on his place, and he made me ginger chicken and rice, and we had a very pleasant evening, free of recriminations or conflict. We had such a good evening, it turned out, that I was still there at half past four in the morning, when the earthquake hit.

One moment I was asleep, and the next I stood naked in the bedroom doorway in the dark while the liquid house moved under my feet, glass crashed all around, and water poured in from the burst pipes in the ceiling. My mind went blank. Scott was the one who ran for Tyrone. The quake went on for an awfully long time, during which I assumed I was going to die, just because everything was moving so violently that it didn't seem possible for it to stop. Then it stopped, and all I heard were water sounds, water hitting glass.

We shook the broken glass off our clothes, put them on, and went outside. All the buildings we could see up and down Hollywood Boulevard were missing chunks, while here and there water geysered up from burst mains. My first thought was that there was no longer such a thing as Los Angeles. My second was that I would not be able to get a cup of coffee.

I took Tyrone, and he and I went to sleep on a blanket in the back of Scott's pickup, while Scott milled about in the road with a flashlight, talking to the neighbors. Later, when the sun was fully up, you could see right through the walls of the house where the plaster and the stucco had come down in sheets. We got in the truck to have a look around and found out within a couple of blocks that L.A. was all still there, surprisingly intact given the state of Hollywood Boulevard. As we drove, I kept peering down side streets looking for damage, and when there was none, I experienced an uneasy sense of deflation—I was disappointed. I didn't say anything. It wasn't nice, probably, to be disappointed that the city hadn't been demolished, and maybe "disappointed" isn't the right word; it was anticlimatic.

We stopped and got some cappuccino at a doughnut shop on Franklin. Then we drove to Koreatown to have a look at my place.

Nothing had even fallen off a shelf there; two thin cracks in the dining room ceiling were the only evidence of a quake.

Scott moved in with me. We made jokes about fate, and then quickly said it was temporary, and then fell into long "but what if" pauses.

The first thing I noticed was that my place seemed smaller, with him in it. My big, cavernous apartment felt like the playhouse my grandfather built for me when I was five, everything miniature and enchanted. Now whenever I cooked in the kitchen, or when we lay in bed reading, or sat together at the enormous dining table, I felt as if I was playing make-believe. I had lived with lots of guys—including Scott—and I'd never had this queer storybook sensation before. Not that I trusted it; I found the preciousness alarming, in fact, like an involuntary sentimental tic.

I got it into my head right away to plant flowers in the strip of yard down in front of the building, and spent hours on my knees digging up weeds and sowing seeds. I bought clay pots for my balcony and planted them with herbs and green beans and tomatoes. I asked other people if they had been feeling an urgent need to dig in the earth after the quake, but they all said no. But I wasn't really bothered about the earth. What troubled me was that my reaction had been to want a cup of coffee. And that I'd been disappointed that it wasn't worse. This was the real reason I was compulsively planting marigolds, me who'd never done anything but kill a plant with a withering glance. It was pure guilt.

Scott's crazy landlady was taking her time getting the building repaired, and the weeks went by. Scott and I began to discuss staying together. We made all the obvious jokes about how the earth moved, and said, "But really, what do you think?" Tyrone was confused. If Scott and I touched each other, he'd come and get between us, pushing us apart.

Then one day we got into an argument over who should pay for the videos we'd rented, and minutes later, after a blindingly nasty exchange that probably lasted about as long as the quake had, it was suddenly and clearly all over. The argument wasn't reasonable, it wasn't well handled but was indicative of many other things, and we both knew it.

Quite soon after the video rental, Scott moved back to his old apartment, where he could camp until the repairs were made, and once again I got that sense of deflation, just like I'd felt after the earthquake, though this time I noticed the equal if not greater measure of relief that went with it.

It wasn't that I was sorry Los Angeles hadn't succumbed to the quake, that thousands and thousands of people hadn't died slow, painful deaths under heaps of rubble; it was that for a moment, I was in a story that was happening, and then all of a sudden, there was no story, and I was back in my life.

Two Pool Parties at the Château Marmont

Esther Williams

"Oh, if this pool could talk," one wizened old broad remarked. The mermaids were already beginning to turn blue around the gills. Every time their barque of lilies and banana leaves drifted near the edge, one of them reached out with the end of her green tail and gave a shove, and the whole bobbing arrangement drifted aimlessly about again. They were terribly young, one Asian, one pinky-pale, more fit for the state fair than for the louche, over-experienced pool of the Château Marmont on Sunset Boulevard.

Not much is left of the Sunset Strip, now that Schwab's and the Trocadero are gone, replaced more or less by Tower Records and the charmingly named Virgin MegaStore, but the Château still reigns over its own bend in the road, a quiet, chalky edifice over-grown by somber foliage and as nicely worn out as a much-handled hundred-dollar bill. People like Myrna Loy used to live here. John Belushi died in one of the bungalows. It still has a timeless, sentimental heroin feel; it's a slum for people who have been too rich and too thin for too long. I've been to countless hip, seedy parties at the Château, either in the bungalows, or up in the suites overlooking Hollywood, or down by the pool.

Esther Williams was late. I'd worn a fifties cerise cocktail dress with a floaty chiffon train and curled my hair with heat rollers, but the cold was beginning to unravel me; I felt brittle all over, certain something about me would tear, snag, or snap in two. I noticed my own slightly shrill and supercilious laughter punctuating everything the stars around me said, whether it was funny or not.

"Esther always puts on a good party," said Cheryl Crane, who plunged a nine-inch carving knife into gangster Johnny Stompanato's chest in 1958, while Stompanato was fighting with his lover, Cheryl's mother, Lana Turner. Cheryl was very tall and thin and sharp and blond, with razor-sharp shoulder pads, in a tight suit with a short skirt. She had a body like a weapon, I thought, and she scared me, I couldn't help it.

Just about then a young man with dreadlocks walked straight up to me and said, "What's your sign?" I have no idea how he got there.

Then Esther Williams made her entrance. She was stocky but trim, in a black pantsuit with rhinestone-crusted buttons. It was odd to see her walk up a flight of stairs in a pantsuit, rather than rising up atop a column of water in a skintight fish-scale lamé suit.

A spry codger in a tux snapped my picture. "Did you see those poor girls in the pool?" he said. "They must be a couple of ice cubes! I'm George Sidney, and this is my wife, Corinne."

Corinne Sidney was just the kind of knockout middle-aged dame you want to be when you grow up: tough, blond, cute, full of pampered piss and vinegar.

"I did Esther's first screen test," said George. "I put her into a dress, and she turned, and I cut the camera and put her into a bathing suit, and she turned, and I put her back in a dress, so she was going around, turning and turning. They saw the test in the front office, and they said, 'That girl is a very dramatic talent!' "

George paused to blow kisses across the pool. "Hello, darling!" he cried. "Kiss, kiss!"

He turned back to me. "Someone got an idea that maybe we could put this youngster with Clark Gable. So they said, 'You've got to make another test.' We were shooting a Western with Clark. Of course, Clark doesn't know the scene; he's just reading it. He comes in and says, 'How do you want it?' Because we had numbers for the kisses. I said, 'Medium, champ.' And he said okay, and he gave her the medium kiss. And don't forget, this girl is sitting there, she's from San Francisco, from the water show, her feet are still wet."

"They had Sonja Henie at Twentieth Century—on ice," Corinne said in her smooth, sassy 1940s voice, "so George decided he was going to have a wet dream."

George snapped another picture of me. "I have over one million photographs," said the eighty-year-old Oscar winner.

Suddenly, the crowd parted and I was right next to Esther. Her eyes were bright apple green. "What do you think of the mermaids?" I asked.

A press of young women closed round us, listening in. They were D girls and PR girls, agents' assistants and the like, the unglamorous, very romantic girls who drift to Hollywood with their B.A.s and two-year internships in advertising or radio, looking for "jobs in the entertainment industry." Esther took them all into her circle and basically treated me as their point man.

Esther made a face, rolled her eyes, and laughed her noisy-broad laugh. "I wanted to put them into retro swimsuits, because I have some that are like what Dietrich wore at the Garden of Allah; in fact, I'm not boasting when I say that when my 1990 swimsuit line came out— You know you're shivering?" Esther squeezed my frigid fingers.

"My fingernails are purple!" One of the gaggle of girls around us squealed, perhaps hoping for a squeeze of her own.

"I think it's because you're all on diets," Esther said. "You need a good, solid meal!"

She raised her wineglass and took a draft. "Daryl Hannah's the only one I ever saw that had a flexible tail that looked like it could *operate*, and I'll bet somebody like an engineer— Howard Hughes, you know, brought in an engineer to *engineer* Jane Russell's bra for *The Outlaw,* because she wanted to wear nothing, and of course we had a thing called the Hayes Office in those days, and Jane was *very* well endowed. Probably still is."

I wondered if most of the girls here even remembered Jane Russell hawking the Playtex "18-hour Cross Your Heart bra" in the late sixties, early seventies. Probably not.

"And because he had Hughes Tool corporation and TWA, Howard Hughes had an engineer come in," Esther went on. "Jane has told me this story and I think it's the most adorable story I've ever heard—an engineer with calipers, measuring things, 'nipple to armpit,' 'nipple to sternum.' I said to Jane, 'How did you like that meeting in the office of Howard Hughes?' "

Esther was distracted by some commotion at her periphery; a man with an Instamatic was trying to get her attention.

"You know the ending of this story?" she asked him archly, freezing him with a look. "You are stopping me because you know the ending? You were an engineer at one time?"

"*I* want to know the ending!" one of the D girls moaned in near desperation.

"Why are you stopping me?" Esther purred. "Because of that stupid *camera?* No!" Esther raised a finger. "Well, I've got to tell you something you never, *never* do with a celebrity, is stop them in the middle of a story! Jump in the pool first, but don't ever do that!"

Her eyes fell on the woman who appeared to be the buffoon's date. "And honey," Esther said, "you obviously have more power over him than my charisma!"

She turned back to the girls. "Do you want to know how it ended?"

We all squealed and cooed, "Yesss, yesss, yesss!"

But Esther wasn't finished with him. "You know," she said. "If I can't get your attention with 'From armpit to nipple, from nipple to sternum,' then you are over the hill, man! I have to think that you're still living with your mother!"

"I'm single!" the man groaned in facetious agony. "I'm a monk!" But Esther ignored his silly attempt to participate in his own humiliation.

"Because what happened," she said to us, "is that they invented the underwire. I said, 'Jane, did you *like* the bra?' She said, 'Well, I wore it in the movie, but I threw the goddamned thing in the garbage, because I don't like to wear a bra.' And I said, 'Ha, I bet you wish you had it *nooooww!*' Because tempus est fugitive, you know. I don't stay up there like I did."

"That's a great story," one of the girls chirped. "I mean, look at the Wonderbra, and how crazy it's made everyone."

Esther laughed and waved her wineglass. "Well, of course, they always had those things with a Brillo pad in there, you stuff everything in *there,* and all of a sudden everything's up *here.*" She garroted herself with a finger. "And if it isn't that, it's silicone and it looks as if you have a shingle off your roof inside, because there's a line that comes—" Here she started tracing cartoon bustlines in the air. "And you say, 'Oh, that's a *square* one, I've seen oval ones but that's a *square* one!' The way you can tell when there's something inside is when you see that what's inside is stronger than the lace of a bra. So the bra comes up here around your neck when you move, because this thing inside is winning! That's why actresses like Demi Moore and the ones who have these unbelievable superstructures, they don't want to wear clothes, because they don't feel as if they're undressed! They have a *shingle* there!"

About a month later I received in the mail a note from George Sidney, thanking me for the piece in the *Times* and enclosing a couple of photographs of me and Esther. He also included his and Corinne's press bios, from which I learned that Corinne's mother was a Ziegfeld showgirl, that her first husband owned the Copacabana, and that she was the National Pin-up Girl on the U.S.S. *Nautilus,* the first atomic nuclear submarine, and *Playboy*'s Centerfold of the Fifties Decade.

I keep the photographs on my dressing table, stuck in the frame of the mirror. A boyfriend once asked me, "Is that your mom?" and I said, "No, that's Esther Williams."

Model Party

"Is this a cool party?" someone whispers.

It's a model party. The models are all wearing satin slips, sandals, and cigarettes. The movie stars are wearing wraparound sunglasses. The smell of incense and clove cigarettes and unisex perfume fills the air, and everyone who isn't a model is wearing black. The invitation from Ford Models, Inc., said "Pool Party," and I had in mind lissome babes lounging in the Hockney-blue pool, scissoring their thighs, saltwater boobs floating them along like water wings, but the only swimmer is a six-year-old girl, probably a stray hotel guest.

I've brought my friend Lori along, because her natural demeanor is a kind of two-Chardonnays-to-the-wind élan, and she recognizes even the most obscure celebrities with dead-on accuracy from thirty paces even when she's actually drunk.

"There's Judd Nelson," Lori says. "And Vendela."

Vendela is smaller than you'd think.

Jack Nicholson is standing near a clump of ferns. His wraparounds have reddish lenses, and he looks like a cat crouching in the bushes, ready to pounce on one of the shiny satin models. Or, to judge by his tight-lipped, satisfied grin, he might already have done just that. I watch him to see if he might cough up a sequin or a pair of panties.

Angie Dickinson walks by.

"Brick House" starts to play. "Brick House" has been playing all over town for a month.

"There's Fabio," Lori says. He's a Brick House, or a side-by-side duplex, but he's wearing a jacket that's too big for him. The shoulder pads hang abjectly, outlined by shiny press marks.

"Gerard Depardieu has Oliver Stone over in the corner," Lori informs me. "And he's telling him that his movies are too violent."

"I just want to look at Winona Ryder all night!" a man sighs. Over our heads, a Sunset Boulevard billboard advertises *Little Women*, Winona Ryder and Susan Sarandon leering down at us, huge. We're like little bugs; they're so big and bright. It's awesome: they have serene, virtuous faces, and the biggest tits of all. They're like saints. Party saints.

A PR girl grabs my elbow. "Joey Buttafuoco has just arrived!"

I'm always getting Joey Buttafuoco mixed up with John Wayne Bobbitt in my head; they're the Mike Douglas and Merv Griffin of victims for me. Downstairs on the red carpet, Joey poses while the paparazzi snap his arrival, then climbs back in his white limousine and leaves. He has not been invited to the party.

Back by the pool, Lori's talking to a guy who turns out to be an actor from one of those short-lived nighttime soaps.

"So, is this a cool party?" I ask him.

He looks morose. "I saw a woman with an empty cup with a lime in it," he says. "So I asked her, 'Enjoying your lime?' And she said, 'I'm sucking away.' "

While we're waiting for the valet to get our car, Lori chats up an interior designer she knows. "Oh my!" he exclaims pertly, midsentence, looking up at yet another giant Sunset Boulevard billboard. "Just *look* how big Chris O'Donnell's toes are!"

Valley of the Dongs

One sunny afternoon in November I find myself bumping through the hills of coastal Ventura County in a golf cart, sandwiched between Randy West, my favorite porn star, and Carter Ward, a retired rocket scientist, on assignment for a magazine. Ward has a Jack Palance air about him—he's all done up in denim, with a red bandanna around his neck, and he's owner of the Dry Gulch Ranch, which is a sprawling, luxurious property overlooking the Pacific up at the northern tail end of Malibu. (Jack Nicholson's ranch is right next door.)

Ward has elected to spend his leisure years constructing Western fantasy sets on his property, for use by the Valley's porn industry. We drive a figure eight around a barn and the Mexican Cantina with its hitching post and swinging doors; then we cruise past a clawfoot bathtub surrounded by bales of hay. Ward parks us at the Indian Village, and we have a look inside a teepee: a fire ring surrounded by mattresses.

"Spaghetti porn," I joke as we climb back into the golf cart.

"I prefer to call what I do erotica," Randy says amiably. "I don't like the word 'porno.' "

I disagree. To me, the word "erotica" evokes images of grad students and Henry Miller. Neither do I like the term "pornography," which makes me think of picket lines outside of 7-Elevens and men in black robes banging their gavels. No, I prefer "porn," or "porno," which makes me think of—well, Randy West, for one. I like Randy. He's a strapping, golden-haired, square-jawed boy of forty-seven, one of the reigning luminaries of the porno universe. He's earnest and easygoing, a feckless, larger-than-life middle American icon, something of a cross between Hercules and Opie. There is, thank God, nothing of Henry Miller about him. I imagine sex with Randy is a friendly contest, athletic, lustful, and victorious.

Ward's walkie-talkie squawks: they're ready for Randy on the bunkhouse set, which is a log cabin down in a leafy gully. Kerosene heaters have been set up in the cabin and Randy's costar, Lana Sands, is waiting by the hitching post wearing a maid's costume, smoking a long, skinny cigarette like a Virginia Slim, and smiling. She and Randy are pals. While the crew sets up, they talk about cars.

The director is a big-boned, red-haired woman in her thirties, named Kelly, who started out making documentaries for PBS. She fell into porn by accident, lured to the Valley by its cheap post-production facilities. "I was working on a film on South America; the guy in the editing bay next to me was working on a bondage film. I always considered myself a feminist"—she sighs—"and I'd never seen a porno movie before. Now, of course, it's like anything else."

"Does anybody have a large Phillips?" Guillermo the assistant cameraman calls out, prompting a round of boisterous speculation as to just whose tool is the biggest.

The scene takes almost two hours to shoot. Randy and Lana do it on the bed and on a Western saddle. Kelly calls out alternately for "hard" action or "soft," shooting coverage for what will be two movies: one for softcore cable TV, and another for hardcore video release. Lana's chest is flat as a washboard, something that is wildly unexpected and sexy.

During a break, Randy comes out of the bunkhouse for a smoke and a stretch. Seeing I'm cold, he gives me his jacket, and wraps me in his big arms. He's cuddly and macho, fun to flirt with.

Later, after the light has gone, Randy and I sit on the porch of the ranch house and eat lasagne with Ward and his wife, Maureen. The two of them are like Mom and Pop, and they call the actors "the kids." When I'm introduced as a writer, they assume I write porno scripts. I don't bother to correct them, because I like this spell, sitting there on the porch with the kids in the waning light, a panorama of the Pacific spread out below, feeling part of the cozy-tough subuniverse of Wild West pornography. I listen to Randy's easygoing drawl; he talks about the industry in a joshing, polite manner, very much the hospitable star to the journalist. He's got his own production company, Erotica West—that "erotica" thing again—and makes a series of low-budget "pro-am" videos called Up and Cummers. It sounds like the Bing and Bob road movies, the way he tells it, just a bunch of friends having a little fun in front of a camera, nothing too heavy. The "amateurs" are mostly exotic dancers who want the cachet.

When it's time to go, Randy shows me pictures of his newborn son and a picture of the child's mother on the cover of a porno magazine. Then he gives me a copy of *Up and Cummers #11* to take home. After that Randy gives me a big hug and drives off in his red sports car, puffing on a Marlboro.

☆

Another day, I drive out to Granada Hills to visit a studio that turns out fifty or so "novelty videos" a year. The proprietor, Ed, runs a full-scale operation with soundstage, editing, and production facilities. Ed is a graying biker type with a ponytail and a paunch under his Harley-Davidson T-shirt. He takes me on a tour.

"The police don't come around like they used to in the old days," Ed says, with a hint of nostalgia. "I've had sixteen busts, but all of them over ten years ago. Nothing since. We have certain guidelines. No child pornography, of course; no animals; no nudity below the waist when there's bondage; no foreign objects"—he looks about and picks up a scrub brush—"like this. The guidelines say you cannot use this scrub brush. If we put a dildo on the end, we could use it, because it would be made for that purpose."

The tour ends in the duplicating room, where floor-to-ceiling racks holding a thousand VCRs whir madly round the clock. Ed tells me his wife runs the distribution end, and one of his sons wrote his master's thesis on the porno industry. "Let's just say he took a position that was somewhat critical," he says with a laugh.

Ed leaves me in a standing set for a suburban kitchen, which doubles as a real kitchen when not in use, the counters spread with sandwich fixings and doughnuts. I get a cup of coffee and wander into a tract-house living room with fake plants, a coffee table, bowling trophies on the mantel. Seated on the sofa is an enormous woman, at least three hundred pounds of flesh in a cotton nightie and heavy glamour makeup, studying her lines from a handwritten script.

She's the Fat Lady today, and she gives her name as Eartha Quake. She's a graduate of Pasadena High School, and this is her first porno movie. She's on a break now, after shooting a scene with Ron Jeremy for a director named Horny Henry. "I thought I'd be uncomfortable," she says wonderingly, "with all those people around. But you don't have time to care."

She's happy to put aside her script study and chat. "I found this shop that has dresses my size," she says. "Today I'm going to go and get this red bodysuit, and some Doc Martens to go with it."

I leave Eartha Quake for the soundstage, where I watch Horny Henry shoot a scene where Dick Nasty lands on the planet of the goat people and fucks the goat queen. The sound stage is bare except for a big velvet-and-gilt throne and some gargoyles in the background. The goat queen is played by a chubby, hirsute blond girl named Christine, who's been fitted out by Makeup with a splendidly realistic goatee.

I chat with Dick Nasty while the crew sets up. He's a Brit, a short, blond, pleasant-looking fellow who winkingly pretends to be embarrassed by my presence. "I got the name Dick Nasty because I used to come on the girl's face, and then kiss her afterwards. The women loved it, but all the guys would go, 'God, Dick, that's nasty!' So that's my name."

The tape rolls; stroking her chin locks and leering at Nasty, Christine delivers her one line: "Ever fucked a billy goat?"

For the next hour and a half, they go at it in the throne. Christine looks bored out of her wits, and Dick looks like he's working very hard at his job. I can tell by the body language on set and off that everyone's annoyed by Christine's lumpish, frowning demeanor. When the camera runs out of batteries, Nasty repairs to a corner with a bottle of lotion and maintains his erection until the PA has come back from the supply room with fresh ones, and things can resume. When Dick's ready for the come shot, he signals. Someone brings him an apple box to stand on, and he jerks off in the direction of Christine's face. The room is full of weary anxiety that collapses the moment he starts to spurt. Christine blinks against the jet of cum, screwing her face up in an expression of forbearance bordering on disgust. By now, her bad-sport attitude annoys even me. Nasty finishes, and extraordinarily, a great glob of cum hangs from the end of Christine's nose. Everyone holds their breath, looking at this quivering thing as big as a turkey wattle; it doesn't fall. All at once, everyone cracks up, collapsing all around in paroxysmic laughter, even Christine.

Later, we're all back in the living room, where Christine, now beardless and in lacy lingerie, has another dull moment with Ron Jeremy. Then Ed directs a scene on the same couch, wherein Eartha Quake lies resplendent in her naked tonnage, working an array of dildos and vibrators while she delivers her lines, acting solo. They're all scenes from various movies, as far as I can tell.

When Ed asks Eartha to insert a noisy vibrator all the way, she can't quite reach around her bulk to do so. After a technical pause, Ed frowns and asks her where she's put the vibrator. "Oh, it's right here," she chirps, lifting a breast and whipping the tool out with an accompanying electronic roar. This is clearly brilliant, and Ed starts to ad-lib with the concept, asking Eartha to play hide-and-seek with the vibrator, which whines comically loud and silent as it rolls in and out of her fleshy folds, sounding almost human, to everyone's delight. We are definitely having fun now.

It's a long day. In the end everyone wants to see my tits, so after a lot of comradely protest I let Dick Nasty pull my shirt open while Horny Henry snaps a picture. Christine is very curious to know what it's like not to wear a bra. The boys, though, seem a little embarrassed. "All in fun, you know," they keep saying with sheepish grins. "Only fair."

Finally, full of Wonder bread, doughnuts, and Folger's, I wait by my car for the driveway to clear, smoking cigarettes with one of the makeup men. He complains that he has to drive all the way to Lake Havasu City. I've driven through there before; it's a retirement mecca on the Arizona border. "Do your parents live there?" I ask. He looks at me strangely. "No," he says, "I do."

Could it be, I think, that all anyone in the porn industry wants is a mid-range Honda and a little place in Arizona?

Of course.

Angry

New Ager

⯪ Things have not been going well for me for some time now. I don't know how it happened, but while I wasn't looking, my glib, glamorous L.A. lifestyle devolved into a series of mundane chores punctuated by illness, accidents, and episodes of sexual rejection.

Then I moved, an experience through which I discovered that there is nothing quite like an hour of wrapping wineglasses in sheets of the *L.A. Times* while your assignment for the same paper is three weeks late to induce a state of free-floating anxiety. My hair was falling out, and my skin perpetually smelled like cardboard and newsprint. I broke out in a rash.

I hit bottom for about a week: didn't work, didn't eat, didn't sleep, didn't breathe. Watched cop shows and Japanese pornography, but didn't masturbate. I'd swear I was using only the first couple of branches of bronchioles; my lungs felt full of cement.

When it struck me that I hadn't peed in seventy-two hours, I called my acupuncturist, and she wrote me a prescription for an herb combo called Chai Hu Kuei Chih Tang, which is said to promote blood circulation in the liver and relieve chest distention and moist heat. I drove down to Chinatown to the herb shop, where Dr. Wang made up six packets of assorted bark, pebbles, and nuts, measuring each on an archaic set of apothecary scales. I took the packets home and brewed up a batch; within an hour I could breathe. By the next day, I could feel something like circulation in my body.

I recovered quickly from this feverish *fugue*, began to ingest and excrete again, and settled into a peculiar state of mind, one I'd never quite experienced before. I didn't feel sad, or hurt, or hopeless. No manic episodes presented themselves, no wild emotions arose for me to wallow in. I didn't feel much of anything at all, except for a calm, silvery, sublime sense of infantile rage.

My girlfriend Janine called me every day. "You need to work on your self-esteem," she said. She wanted me to go into therapy.

"No, no," I'd answer disgustedly. "I like myself fine. It's everything else I hate." If only I were filled with self-loathing! On the contrary, my opinion of myself was running rather high. The problem, as far as I could see, was that the world itself was weak and foul, not so much evil as hopelessly autistic.

I was not depressed. I was not neurotic. I was neither paranoid nor delusional. I was in a state of diffuse, de-cathected *hate*. Let me be absolutely clear: while there were people I hated, and things I hated, I was not in hate with any of them in particular. I did not burn with hatred; rather, it was like a dryness on my skin, an absence in the air around me. It was not hot, you see, but cold, this hatred of mine, and the reigning sensation was of feeling far, far less at any given time than I had ever felt before.

After the exercises, we take our mats outside for the meditation, or relaxation, part of the class, and this worries me anew, because unless you count OD'ing on Theraflu, I don't relax. I can't lie down without something to read, because my mind doesn't just wander, it runs around in a frenzy until all its parts are thoroughly bruised and dislocated. Consciousness terrifies me. Sometimes it takes me a long time to recover from a bout of relaxation.

So I'm apprehensive.

"Meditation is something you can't force," Gurmukh says. "Someone once told me it's like trying to take a shit. Pushing doesn't really help." Bear in mind that she sounds like Mr. Rogers when she says this, and the effect is a cut above irony. It makes me want to try to not try to meditate, which is an elaborate enough construct to put me at ease.

True to form, I just manage to endure the session during which Gurmukh tells us to fill our bodies with light while she makes lovely, sonorous howling sounds by rubbing a rubber mallet on a crystal bowl.

Then we're done. I sit up, blinking in the Topanga sun. I listen to my body to see if I'm any more whole or centered than before, then realize that I'm already picking furiously at a scab on my heel. So much for being whole, or even wanting to be so. Still, I have to admit I do feel better. Not emotionally tuned, but two hours older and none the worse for it, which is something I find instructive.

The next day I find myself laughing madly at a book I'm reviewing. The book, a memoir by the infomercial mogul who introduced Suzanne Sommers to the ThighMaster, is so deliciously bad that I howl and rock back and forth and weep tears of side-splitting derision—a set of gestures formally similar to the Kundalini exercise of the day before. . . .

And finally, I have my emotion: my heart beats faster, and I'm suddenly filled with blind affection for a world that could produce anything as ludicrous as this. Gurus, ThighMasters, starlets and serial killers, traffic accidents, Frappuccinos, designer preschools, and the occasional bad date. I think I finally get the New Age and what it means to Angelenos: it's aversion therapy for humanists. I laugh and laugh and laugh. And, like Malcolm McDowell at the end of *A Clockwork Orange,* I'm finally cured.

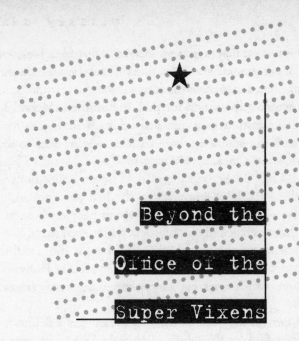

Beyond the Office of the Super Vixens

The strangest thing I've ever seen in my life was a beggar on Chowringhee Road in downtown Calcutta. (To my mind L.A., especially around Hollywood Boulevard, has a certain affinity with Calcutta. Calcutta was built in a malarial swamp. Los Angeles was built in a seismically active desert. Both places are unreasonable, more or less uninhabitable cities.) I was coming out of a shop where I'd just bought a string of lapis lazuli beads. At first I mistook the man for a sadhu in a yogic headstand, but then, as if I'd taken a swift kick in the kidneys, I saw that this man had no head. Rather, his body from the neck up protruded directly from a patch of bare dirt in the middle of the sidewalk, a patch that apparently had been intended for a tree. This man's torso, his arms and legs, did in fact resemble a gnarled tree. There was, so far as I could see, no way for him to breathe, and the earth all around him was tamped down tight. The quality of the earth is essential to the picture: it wasn't the least bit loamy, but dusty and hard, giving the impression that he'd been there like that for a long, long time. Had I not passed that way many times before, I would have thought him a permanent fixture.

I have no explanation for this. It disturbed me, and I am not that easily disturbed by physical oddity. I have seen lepers, and men with elephantiasis whose testicles were swollen to the size of watermelons. Once, a very long time ago, I went to bed with a man I'd met at the opera, and didn't even notice until watching him dress the next morning that he had two stunted, withered legs. As a child, I often dreamed about people whose bodies fell apart like overcooked chickens when I touched them. But nothing ever got to me the way the headless beggar did. I tell the story because it best evokes the way I feel inside the Hollywood Wax Museum, which gives me almost the same creepy frisson of the undead.

Upstairs in the back of the wax museum is a flyblown suite of offices staffed by the family of Punjabi Sikhs who own the museum. These are bilge-colored linoleumed rooms like the ones Philip Marlowe always woke up in with a bump on his head and a bad hangover. The place smells of burnt coffee, ink, and inefficiency. There's seldom anyone there.

A door at the back of the office leads to a dim attic space where row upon row of wax heads is stacked to the ceiling, a purgatorial pantheon where Hollywood has-beens are catalogued in a kind of limbo. Whatever happened to Flip Wilson? He's on the shelf, between Dean Martin and Danny Thomas. A hairless Whoopi Goldberg looks too much like Mahatma Gandhi; the bald Farrah Fawcett is all teeth. Congressman Sonny Bono is wearing a straw hat from another lifetime. A longhaired, dimpled John Travolta looks eager and hopeful, sandwiched between four Hitlers and a Stalin. (This is no place for hubris: the Arnold Schwarzenegger downstairs in the *Terminator* display is using Rex Harrison's old body.)

Here in the belly of Fame there's a patina of stillness over all—not the stillness of photographs, but that of traumatic memory.

What's captured isn't a moment in time, but one of time's volatile moods: it's the kind of thing one "sees" just before a blackout and inevitably fails to remember. The life flashing before your eyes, or just a paramedic's grin.

Under the ranks of heads, the floor space is taken up by a phalanx of generic bodies, called "nondescripts" in the wax biz, part of a cache of TV Holocaust victims the museum picked up on the cheap. Some of these are earmarked to become apostles, replacing the pockmarked assemblage in the museum downstairs, whose faces have suffered from years of the public's penny-pitching antics. A fiberglass dummy with a face that looks like Buster Keaton's has a square of paper taped to its chest that says "Jesus" in ballpoint ink.

I find this place physically poetic, and it's been in my imagination since the moment I first saw it. The images are obliquely, compulsively moving, at once naked, false, epic, and familiar. I can never put my finger on _what_ it is they make me feel—in the end I have to believe that they are primary images, indivisible as primary numbers, the inchoate stuff of dreamscapes. That attic is what I imagine the unconscious to look like, the image that comes to mind at the question "Where do your thoughts go when you're not thinking them?" The answer must be that they go to a place a lot like this.

Moving on: in the very, very back of the attic, at the end of a long hallway, is a low-ceilinged workroom, where a saucepan full of half-melted ears bubbles on a hot plate, while ghoulish wails and moans from the Chamber of Horrors drift up through the floorboards. A pair of troll-like curators work on replacing Tom Selleck and Don Johnson with the cast of _Baywatch_. The head curator, Ken, is a tiny, near-toothless man, and his assistant, Steve, is almost as tiny. Steve changed his last name to Kirk in homage to _Star Trek,_ and he's more or less responsible for the year I spent on Hollywood Boulevard.

I met these two when I was writing up the museum for the _L.A. Times_; it was during one of my visits to their garret that Steve sidled up to me and said, "You know, I'm a writer, too. I keep a little office down the Boulevard."

My eyes must have lit up, because he immediately offered to take me over and show me around. The rent, he said, was fifty dollars a month, and there was space available.

So Captain Kirk and I piled into my Volkswagen and drove down Hollywood Boulevard to a nondescript brick building built in that paranoid sixties style and sandwiched between the freeway and a gas station. "It was red-tagged after the earthquake," Steve said. "That's why it's renting so cheap right now—everyone bailed." There were signs of renovation about, so I decided not to ask further. Earthquakes don't scare me. Escalators scare me, telephones scare me, but not earthquakes—for while I'm very respectful of phobias and other forms of esoteric dread, the fear of calamity has always struck me as undignified. To me, the building's seismic status was unimportant, and if Kirk said the landlord was "fixing it up," then that was good enough for me. The upside, Kirk told me, was that the cowardly lemmings who'd abandoned ship after the quake had left behind loads of office furniture, which was now free for the taking.

While we waited for the elevator, I eyeballed the directory. The building was still largely empty, but already there were a travel agent, a lawyer, a satellite company, some unidentified individuals, a church group, an immigration service, and the editorial offices of the *Beirut Times*.

On the third floor, the cigar smoke was thick in the brown-carpeted hallway that ran past the *Beirut Times* office and down the length of the building, off it little bays with a multitude of numbered doors. Kirk opened number 308C, and we were in what looked like the world's smallest museum. He'd built a platform all along the room's perimeter, and along it a number of life-sized mannequins displayed his collection of costumes from various sci-fi productions, his prize being a genuine Superman cape once worn by Christopher Reeve. The displays were beautifully lit, but the space itself was no bigger than a large storage room. In the middle

was a metal-and-Formica desk, and beyond that, there was barely
room to stand. This was where Kirk wrote his sci-fi scripts. He
also ran a celebrity-impersonator agency on the side, he said,
though so far he had only Charlie Chaplin (himself) and a part-
time Madonna.

The office that was available was right next to his, a stark, closet-
like cube that, under the harsh fluorescent light, looked like a place
you wouldn't want to be left alone without a straitjacket.

"Are there any others?" I asked. "With windows, maybe?"

"Oh, but they're all much bigger, much more expensive," Kirk
assured me. "No, this is the best one for you." Only later would
I realize (with great sympathy) the desperate lengths one would
go to in order to obtain a sane neighbor in these environs.

I squinted. With furniture and a lamp, it might just be fine. Kirk
promised to call the landlord and put in a good word for me, and
we walked back to the elevator.

The elevator door groaned open to take us down, releasing an
odor that was an odd concoction of chicken broth and urine, and
out popped a half-naked, grinning urchin with wild gray corkscrew
hair and beady blue eyes above a shirtless potbelly. It stared at me
as if I were a Christmas cookie, gave a snuffly little grunt like a
piglet, then shuffled off down the hall, barefoot. That, Kirk explained, was the attorney. "He's got six dogs living in his car."

I dropped Kirk back at the wax museum and drove home, more
enamored by the minute of the dismal, rickety, smoky, dog-
infested office building.

There was one problem: at the time, I didn't happen to have
fifty dollars, so I said I'd think about it, and went on my way. At
home I called my friend Nancy, who was also a writer, had a small
child, and worked at home.

Nancy was a Wesleyan girl from a good family; she came to
Hollywood to be an actress, then abandoned that for writing
screenplays. Along the way she'd spent seven years in love with a
Native American actor, with whom she'd had a daughter. When
I met her, she'd given up on screenwriting and had just published

her first piece of journalism, a long first-person account of a road trip she'd taken with a friend of hers who had been pen pals with John Wayne Gacy, to meet the man before his execution. I was writing nightlife for the "Life and Style" section of the *L.A. Times*. Nancy took me to a weird little cocktail lounge in a Denny's restaurant in Glendale, and we'd been good friends ever since, though there's no reason for it. Nancy is dark and frizzy-haired, runs marathons, and talks so fast she's sometimes called the Human Hummingbird, whereas I am generally pale, soft-spoken, and limp.

"Listen, Nance," I said, "if you like the cocktail lounge at Denny's, you'd love this office."

"Well," Nancy said when I'd described the setup. She was entirely in sympathy with my state of mind and pocket. "I don't have fifty dollars either. The question is, do you have twenty-five?"

Two days later, we went to pay our deposit and get the keys from the landlord, a biker named Rusty. Rusty had a wooden leg, a long red beard, a noble belly, and usually one or two of his old lady's kids trailing after him. He was, be it noted, a wealthy, property-owning biker who had won several Emmys for film editing and took his road trips not through hick towns in backwoods America, but through Europe. He acted, too, and I still see him on TV once in a while, in roles with script notations such as "Biker Dude #3." But Rusty was a real biker, and no one would ever have mistaken him for a weekend warrior, not for a heartbeat.

Rusty was also a soft touch, and treated his tenants with paternal forbearance, even the less-than-savory ones. We sat in his office on the second floor while he cut us an extra set of keys.

"Get that cat out of here, I mean it now, that's the last time I'm going to tell you!" he shouted at a skinny old woman skulking through the hallway, the mother of a family of heroin addicts who had taken up residence. She caught hold of her skinny tabby cat, smiled fleetingly, and minced away. Rusty shook his head. "That one's been rode hard and put away wet a few times too many," he said fondly. "Remember," he said with an utterly straight face as we prepared to go, "this is a nonsmoking building."

Our tiny office turned out to be just like one of those miniature automobiles that always seem to have room for one more clown. We each occupied a corner with a desk and a file cabinet, and there was a good three feet of wide-open space between us once we'd settled in. We hung Christmas lights, arranged some pink vinyl chairs around a minuscule coffee table by the door, and found that there still seemed to be plenty of space to set up the pink-and-black fifties bar I'd picked up from the Salvation Army and never quite found a place for. One of Nancy's many fly-by-night fiancés, a conceptual artist I think, came in to hang our shelves and christened us Beyond the Office of the Super Vixens.

We had our first cocktail party that same Friday, inviting a few friends to drop by and running across the street to Liquor to Go-Go for ice and pretzels. For the first hour or so of the party, it was just us two, which suited us fine. We mixed gin martinis and put our feet on our desks. Nancy had on a silver miniskirt, and I think mine was red. (Martinis at five, we later realized, was not such a good idea, and on the next Friday Nancy switched to Campari and soda, and I to beer.) But after the first beverage, we were pleased as punch with our coup and giggling like children.

"The best bar in Los Angeles," Nancy said.

"Fabulous," I agreed.

Super Vixens' Dymaxion Lounge, as Friday evening came to be called, did not exactly turn into a coveted invitation, though it was a definite success. We called it the Dymaxion Lounge in homage to Buckminster Fuller, inventor of the Dymaxion House, the Dymaxion Car, and the Dymaxion Map. A Dymaxion thing has everything you need, right where and when you need it. The whole idea reflects an optimistic, nostalgic, twentieth-century futurism, in which everything is well designed, everyone has enough to eat, and work is a pleasurable exercise of one's essential being. Fuller believed in God and wrote poetry when he wasn't inventing. He ate a rare steak every day. Everything he did seemed to fail through accidents of fate. He summered on an island, where he used to take visitors out to the shoreline and tell them that if they looked at the horizon long enough, they could see the earth revolve on its axis. They always saw it, to Fuller's delight. The cocktail parties, we hoped, would be a little like Fuller's island weekends, a little harmless vixenry where the axis of the earth was concerned. In short, we declared ourselves fabulous, and waited to see whom we could get to agree. It worked.

Right away we realized the impossibility of inviting our friends. After all, we were two to begin with, and no more than six or seven could ever hope to fit into our broom closet of a bar, even assuming that two or three would spill into the hallway. Even if we took turns, no single cross section of either of our acquaintances would fit. The results was that we mostly entertained people we did not know, strays we picked up here or there, or friends of acquaintances. I can't remember their names or what they looked like, just snippets of conversation and the things they left behind. There were always one or two members of Nancy's barfly hipster softball team, these young, virginal guys who wrote poetry or were English. A rare-book collector with an Elvis jumpsuit brought us a bottle of grappa for the bar. And a giant Canadian who was just back from Burma stood everyone dinner at Musso & Frank, though no one knew who he was until my friend Janine showed up hours later and introduced him. Bill Higgins, who covers society for the *Times*, came in looking ashen in his khakis and Hawaiian shirt, and announced that our building had been the draft board in the sixties, which seemed to explain the predominance in the layout of windowless cubicles.

The office thrived. Nancy and I seemed both to bring in more work now that we had a headquarters. We grew. Our winking, see-the-earth-spin attitude got us a Super Vixen corporate account at American Express. On a whim one weekend, we bought a cute little rustic cabin at Big Bear Lake for our "company retreats."

The Super Vixen era, as we now call it, peaked when we were

hired as a team to write a trashy book about a TV show, which resulted in the Dymaxion Business Trip. Suddenly, we found ourselves lodged in a suite at the Four Seasons Hotel in New York, where we jumped on the beds like children, reviewed the martinis, and invited all our magazine editors to the grandest Dymaxion Lounge of all. Oh, what a time we had.

That hotel suite had an unfortunate viral effect on us, for shortly after our return, we sashayed into Rusty's office and told him we wanted a big old suite on the fourth floor. Now we had gray carpet instead of brown, windows (frosted glass, but close enough), a reception area, and a separate room for the bar, which we promptly decked out in mirror tile and paper lanterns. We each had our own office now, and while Nancy stuck to vinyl and Venetian blinds, I went out and got a sofa, a cowhide rug, used drapes out of some bankrupt motel, and a desk as big as Texas. I felt like a cattle baron.

But somewhere along the line, our arrogance had offended the Dymaxion gods. The air conditioning in the new office never worked, and we baked like ants under a magnifying glass. We both unaccountably started smoking like chimneys, and left dirty ashtrays all around. We took to eating Power Bars for lunch and mixing instant coffee from lukewarm tap water. My sofa was always covered by great drifts of paper, and my desk drawers filled up with dirty underwear and changes of sweaty evening clothes I never managed to take home. I hung hardware for bookshelves and never put up the boards, so that the metal brackets stuck out from the walls like a torture device for an Inquisition waiting to happen. We both hooked up with loser boyfriends who left semen stains on the carpet and complicated, emotional messages on the answering machine. At a certain point, we looked at each other and bailed, closing the office down almost as quickly as we'd opened it.

The Super Vixen era was exciting, if slight. I didn't meet anyone interesting or do anything important, or entertain a single profound or complicated thought. I made lots of money, but seemed to have nothing to show for it. At the end of our first year, I felt as if we'd planned and executed an elaborate jewel heist. It was, I suppose, worth it for that: I grew used to thinking of myself as getting away with something, which sensation alone was well worth a year of my life.

So ended the Dymaxion Relationship. Nancy and I were tired of looking at each other's haircuts, anyway. We weren't Hope and Crosby anymore, but that bad married couple who nag each other in the middle of a dinner party when they're in a black mood, and finish each other's sentences when they're feeling in the pink. Not pretty.

In the end, the dissolution was for the best; we would have ended up as motivational speakers or talk-show hosts. Instead, we had the thirty-year-old's equivalent of Junior Year Abroad.

☆

I still like to go down to Mann's Chinese whenever there's a "big" movie opening. I'm a sucker for steroids and shrapnel, and the Chinese has the best screen in town. I always get a kick out of the tourists who uncap their video cameras to film the movie stars' handprints in the concrete out front of the theater. "Hello"—you want to say—"nothing's *moving* here!"

Then you feel tacky for scoffing at the tourists, because the whole thing is for them, for them and the runaways. Hollywood is for tourists and runaways; they both stare at the pavement a lot, because there isn't much else there, beside them.

It goes like this: you know the dream, where you're in your second-grade class, and all of a sudden you realize that you're *naked?* That dream is what Hollywood Boulevard is all about: the dreadful simultaneity of fame and shame. They're the same thing, of course, just varieties of exposure. Desire and fear, the same again.

These are things it's impossible to bear in mind from moment to moment. Memory and movement: now, those are genuine opposites. Half those names on the Walk of Fame—no one remembers who they are. They are nothing, carved in stone. On a street where no one goes, except to take a picture of the street.

The tourists with the video cameras are right, of course: the only thing worth recording is that long, fixed gaze itself.

Drag Divas

Last Christmas Nancy and I threw a Christmas party at the Grand Star restaurant in Chinatown, with lots of greasy noodles, booze, and karaoke. Nancy belted out "Delta Dawn," while I essayed "That Old Black Magic." The party was fabulous and so was I, in my red dress from Frederick's of Hollywood, high heels, and rhinestones. Scott came, only to sit on a bar stool laughing at me all night and hitting on my girlfriends. At the end of the evening he said, "I hope you aren't offended by this, but I think I've figured you out. The thing about you is, you're like a man pretending to be a woman. You're in drag!"

Far from being offended, I found this assessment too flattering. First in my mind, of course, was the satisfaction of knowing that I frightened the hell out of him with my *cojones*. But when I started to think more deeply about it, I had to agree that my take on femininity is indeed magnificently superficial—all platinum locks, false eyelashes, lipstick, and patent leather. Which is not to say that it isn't necessary. Leave me naked on a desert island and I would turn into ... well, I don't know exactly. A woman, a man, a dog, a tree? Actually, I'd probably die in the first week, trying to pound some poisonous berries into lip rouge.

But in reality, Scott's comment had less to do with his having glimpsed my soul fumbling with its anima down than with the recent Season of the Drag Queen. What happened was, Hollywood discovered RuPaul, and suddenly every supper club in town had to have a drag queen as hostess. Educated people began to overuse the word "drag" the way my friends in college had overused "deconstruction"—and the two seemed to end up meaning roughly the same thing, in good time.

So, when my friend Rob proposed a weekend outing to Dragstrip 66, the venerable Silverlake club that happens once a month in one of those ubiquitous L.A. venues with bad eighties decor, I was ready to tag along. The theme this month was "Vegas Showgirls," and we decided, after rejecting Cleopatra and Pocahontas, to go with a Madame Wong look.

Two years earlier, Rob and Philip would have borrowed my dresses if they needed to do drag. This year, their Christmas card had a picture of the two of them in full alter-id.

Rob is a thirty-year-old white boy most of the time, but on the occasional Saturday night he becomes, in corkscrew wig and hippie skirt, a dead ringer for a mulatto poetess with an MFA from Antioch, whose name is Tante Livonia. Rob's always the most beautiful boy in the room, very shiny and neat and poised and canny and witty. Last time we went to a cocktail party together, the bartender reached out, touched his bronze bicep, and said, "You have such lovely skin—do you mind me asking what you use?" Tante Livonia, on the other hand, is a messy girl. She doesn't wear lipstick or perfume, and she lounges around a table in silence, like a sullen Siamese cat.

Philip ordinarily strikes one as a forty-six-year-old Old Etonian à la Kim Philby—a natty gentleman with graying temples, who has something worsted about him even when he turns up at my house for Sunday brunch in shorts and T-shirt. As Lady Foote-Lockre, he dons a blond wig to become a vision in Chanel equivalents. "I always carry an air of upper-class nymphomania," she sniffs, fanning herself so that curls of chest hair dance amid the bright red marabou of her off-the-shoulder gown. The gesture suggests she may be getting the first inkling of those hot flashes associated with "the change."

I interviewed them once for a story on drag, and even though they weren't dressed at the time, they immediately lapsed into character.

"Drag puts you out of sympathy with the feminist agenda," Foote-Lockre said in her benign, hoity-toity way, "in that you want the attention. You expect your drinks to be paid for. You don't want convenient pockets in clothing. You don't want sensible shoes!"

"I want that!" Livonia objected crossly. "I want to go barefoot and wear no underwear and a flouncy skirt! And to not have to shave my armpits!"

Lady Foote-Lockre looked patient. "But surely you don't want a pocket?"

Livonia considered this. "I—I don't want to have to need a pocket," she said somewhat awkwardly.

Lady Foote-Lockre smiled (if you think Tante Livonia is a pill, you should meet Helga, the persona Rob adopts when it's time to clean the apartment), and said, "Also, drag is the only pleasurable form of self-consciousness."

☆

At noon on Saturday, I met Rob at his apartment on the second floor of a building called the Happy Malaga Castle. It's a Spanish stucco affair from the twenties; Gloria Swanson used to meet her lover there. "Bad news," he said when he answered the door. "Conjunctivitis."

Sure enough, it was a bad case of pinkeye. "I think China girls are out," he said. "I shouldn't be wearing eye makeup."

So we decided to opt for a generic late-fifties off-duty-showgirl look, which could include sunglasses. Then we ate one of Rob's leftover pasta creations for lunch, sitting on the edge of the bed and watching a Japanese movie called *Vengeance Is Mine*. I never liked Japan until I met Rob. The way the people would sit and kneel, sit and kneel, sit and kneel, just in the process of, say, opening and closing a door, that always made me want to scream. But Rob lived in Japan for a couple of years, and he's taught me that the Japanese are as viscous on the inside as they are brittle on the outside, and now I adore Japanese movies and novels and food. Early on in the movie, the hero killed a man, then washed the blood from his hands by pissing on them, which was breathtaking.

After lunch, we went to Ozzie Dot's, where we found Rob a spangly sleeveless shell with a beaded fringe, which would go perfectly with my white vinyl capri pants. (Rob and I had discovered that we wore the same size one night when I needed an escort for a black-tie event and stuffed him into my Brooks Brothers tux.) Next we drove down Hollywood Boulevard until we found the shoe store that stocked ladies' shoes for men. Being expert in the ergonomics of high heels, I tried everything on first in my size, passing judgement on each shoe's cant and stability. "It's not the height of the heel," I explained, "but how the shoe is balanced." We settled on a pair of black patent-leather pumps that would go with everything. "Ninety dollars," Rob remarked, looking at the price tag on the box. We contemplated this commitment in silence for a moment, but there was no way out. Tante Livonia's clogs were not going to work this time. Rob paid for the shoes, and on the way out we stopped at a souvenir shop and bought him a pair of gold hoop earrings the size of bicycle rims, and some Jackie O sunglasses. Then we each went home and took a nap.

At nine o'clock we reassembled at my place, laid out our gear, and had a martini, this to steel us for the first event of the evening, which involved an obligation to hear a friend of Rob's debut as a torch singer at a bar in Hollywood. Arriving just in time, we sat

down at a big table with a bunch of people, some of whom I knew
and some of whom I didn't. Rob's friend the singer took the mike.

She was a mousy redhead, a middle-aged Pippi Longstocking
out of place in a severe black cocktail dress. She looked hostile,
but this could have been part of the act. With hunched, tense
shoulders she bent her head over the mike the way people who've
spent time in jail hunker protectively over a plate of food while
they eat. She started with a sullen rendition of "Skylark."

What happened next was something so rare and bizarre that it
now seems like a dream to me, and I can only think that I must
have been transported into a hypnagogic stupor by pain so intense
it defies the light of memory. I don't really know how bad the
singing was, because I can't remember a single note of it. I remember the first long minutes of trying to fix my attention, then
a long, amorphous swath of time spent struggling for any kind of
consciousness at all, and finally, the whole group's sudden and
unanimous breakdown. Some chattered, some fled; one person actually walked up to her and stopped her to offer some coaching,
after which she was slightly louder, if no less baleful. By the end
of her first set, most of her friends had fled the building, and Rob
and I did, too.

At home, we had another martini and set about our toilettes.
My days as a beauty writer meant I had a good supply: false eyelashes, foundations, makeup sponges, glittery eyeshadow, and from
one comparative study, around a hundred shades of red lipstick.
From a story I never actually wrote for *Cosmo*, I had ended up
with three wigs: one long Coppertone blond; one perky *That Girl*
brunette; and one curly Andrews Sisters red.

We put Etta James on the CD player and pulled everything out
of my closets, out of the drawers, trying on headgear and scarves
and jewelry and gloves and littering the floor with tissues smeared
with every shade of lipstick. It was like shopping, but at night,
with music and martinis: a shopping nightclub.

Rob wound up in the brunette flip and Chanel Vamp lipstick,
with the gold hoops and the Jackie O glasses, the white vinyl

capris, and the spangly shirt and heels. At the last minute we added some gloves and a gold handbag.

I put on black fishnets, heels, and a whaleboned fifties maillot in an ornate gold-and-purple paisley print. I put on the Andrews Sisters wig and tied it up with a blue organza head scarf, and set about with martini-fueled vigor to make my face as masklike as possible. I powdered my face white, roughed my cheeks, drew my brows into little bows, slathered on three pairs of Ardell lashes above and below, applied three layers of lipstick with dusting powder in between, and drew a mole on my cheek. Looking at myself in the mirror, I could almost see it, I was almost *in drag*. I pawed through my makeup drawers, hunting for inspiration, and came across a pot of shocking blue powder I'd bought at a drugstore for a dollar but had never worn. That was it, I realized, the girl thing a girl wouldn't think to do. Blue eyeshadow.

"Wow," Rob said when I finally came out of the bathroom.

We made it to Dragstrip at about one in the morning, and by two, we were ready to go. But that's how it always is; the main thing about drag is doing it. The public spectacle is a mere excuse for the mirror-communion of being able to dress and dress and dress with abandon. Once you get there, it's all over quick.

Rob and I roamed together, strutting and ogling; then we split up and roamed some more; then we hung out on the patio together for a while, cooling off and resting our sore feet—Rob's from his first high-heel experience, mine from the rare bite of fishnet stockings grinding a grid of blisters into the balls of my feet. And then we left, ready for the *grand dénouement*.

On the way out, the valet who brought Rob's Volkswagen Jetta around looked at us and shook his head slightly. As he held my door for me, I asked, "Do you think I'm a man or a woman?" He shook his head again and said, "I don't know anymore."

We drove to the mall that housed the Yukon Mining Co., a vaguely Wild West–themed twenty-four-hour coffee shop that has long been an after-hours hangout for drag queens. I'd first been here a couple of years back, with Rob and Philip and the nineteen-

year-old boy who was adoring Rob at the time. We'd all been to
Dragstrip, also arriving very late. Rob and his protégé were dressed
as nature boys, in loincloths and vines, Philip was wearing my
zebra-print halter sheath, and I had made an attempt to dress as
a guy, in a blue three-piece suit, my dark blond hair made dirty
and stringy, my eye sockets darkened, eyebrow-pencil stubble on
my face. I looked like Kato Kaelin. All I remember of that night
is that little Nature Boy fell asleep and snored, his nose hanging
an inch above his mashed potatoes.

We sat down in a booth and ordered the usual: a club sandwich
for Rob, no mayo, and a hot turkey sandwich for me, spongy white
bread and whipped potatoes under a scary, gelatinous glob of
brown gravy—four A.M. ballast. There was another table near us,
of older, more accomplished drag queens in serious full-body
makeup, evening gowns, and lamé headdresses, but we were too
scared to talk to them, and they left soon after our food came. By
the time we finished eating, we realized we were in fact the only
drag queens left. A few sad elderly locals hung at the counter; a
Latino couple at the end of a very late date sat in a corner booth.
The graveyard help was transferring old ketchup from one Heinz
bottle to another and yawning.

"Poor Pippi Longstocking," Rob said.

"Yes," I said, "poor Pippi." Then, instead of fading, we
launched into a discussion of performance art, arguing over
whether the comedian Andy Kaufman had faked his own death.
Before we left, we wrote "Andy Kaufman is alive!" on a piece of
napkin, rolled it up, and stuck it in the pepper shaker.

Weeks later, Rob reported back to me some surprising news:
"Someone told me Pippi Longstocking had a penis! We'd always
wondered, but he accidentally brushed up against it, and he says
she definitely has a penis."

"I had no idea," I said, and I really hadn't. Her surly-spinster
demeanor had been too enigmatically dyspeptic for anyone to con-
sider that it might be a gender display. I began to wonder whether
Pippi really had a penis or was wearing a fake one under her

widow's weeds just to provoke such gossip, and whether the whole bad-songbird-thing had really been a highly effective and cruel prank on a bunch of gullible friends. I began to like her right away, for her very opacity, and the way in which she was or wasn't herself and either way wasn't terribly likable, and I thought how the whole thing about drag is to be despised and loved at once—to be a cruel beauty, and vulgar and grand. And I liked Rob and Philip and me with our mutually endearing peccadilloes and our shrill, annoying co-optation of everything we see that we *like*, including drag. The world stood revealed as one big walk-in closet— and it was full of beautiful, shimmery things.

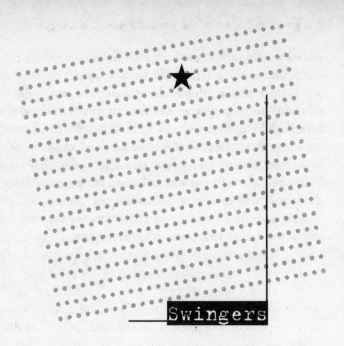

Swingers

I once had an affair with a couple. They joked a lot about their "tempestuous relationship," together and separately, and courted me according to that model, though I courted them right back with a certain faux tempestuosity of my own.

I'd been schooled in the loose from a tender age: the first sounds of sex I remember hearing from my bed as a child were those of my mom and my dad's cousin, a pairing that began and ended shortly after my parents' divorce; and the first time I saw a "grown-up" movie I was nine and my baby-sitter took me down to see *Bob & Carol & Ted & Alice*. I fell asleep in the middle, as I'm famously reminded from time to time by childhood intimates who know the story, but something salient from that feature must have crept in. So it was that when the opportunity to swing fully presented itself, I was less than immune.

These two were fascinating to me. I once saw him throw a chair across a room, and it seemed like a transcendently correct action, an accurately unmitigated response to a bad phone call about a check that wasn't coming on time—why not?

One night I had a dream about the two of them, which involved a hot tub and lots of seventies sex. Shortly thereafter, though neither of them really drank, I lured them out to the Grand Star on Karaoke night, and plied them with my version of "Making Whoopee." Since I can't carry a tune, my version of the song consists of lots of breathy phrases, punctuated by grunts, pants, and pre-orgasmic squeals. Somewhat drunk, they drove me back to my car downtown, and I told them all about the hot-tub dream. We ended up in a three-way on a deserted corner in Little Tokyo, while a homeless guy across the street watched pensively and the car engine idled. After that, we started to date.

They took me out to dinner at a nice restaurant, and the first sign of trouble, though I ignored it, was that she circled the car after we parked, to make sure we all had locked our doors.

The sex, later at my apartment, was *fun*. I'd never done this before, and it was a frizzy shock to be in bed with two, doing things I had never done. I'd forgotten how much fun sex could be when it's new, a precipice over which you skein yourself, hopeful of no end of permutations to keep you going on with the momentum you've started, uncomplicated by anything but the daunting physical arrangements. It was hugely fun: like getting to have high school sex again, in my thirties.

Afterward, the overnight thing started to be a problem. She wanted to know if I had dental floss, and I didn't. Neither did I have the special face cream without which she would not sleep. I got the idea, and so did he, and they left, gathering their shoes and overcoats and so on in an urgent haze.

The next time we went out, she'd brought everything with her, in an overnight bag. When we finished in bed, she dressed to go get it from the trunk of her car, but with particular emotional urgency. When she walked out of the bedroom, I didn't think she was coming back. I wouldn't have, had I been her. He and I stayed in bed for twenty minutes, alone together. We didn't fuck,

then we fucked, then we didn't fuck. I didn't think she was
coming back. He put on his clothes, saying she was outside,
and went to get her. She was outside, and he got her. They came
back, with her overnight bag, and the three of us fucked; in the
middle, they began to argue. He hadn't penetrated me before in
front of her, and at a certain point he was about to, and looked
at her, and then didn't. Then he fucked her hard, and after everyone had come, he stormed out of the bedroom. Then he came
back.

I got up to take some NyQuil, and while I was at the sink, she
said, "We're sorry, we both had fucked-up childhoods." The
covers were tucked up under her chin.

"That's okay," I said. "I have a three-year-old, I'm used to this
kind of behavior."

I hadn't meant it to be ironic, and it wasn't taken so. They didn't
mind.

We all got in bed to sleep. Then we had sex again. After, she
got up out of the bed and threw her clothes on with contained,
upset gestures. She left. "I thought she was this bohemian spirit,
like me," he said, "but in the end she turned out to be—so *bourgeois*." Then we fucked, and then he went after her, in the nude.
She was smoking a cigarette in the stairwell.

They came back. We all fucked again, and afterward *he* got up
in a cataclysmic huff and dressed, throwing his leather coat on and
blistering out of the bedroom. I put on my silly polyester negligee
and followed him down the hallway, catching up in the living
room.

"Don't you dare leave me alone here with this," I said, and
meant it.

He came back to bed. Eventually, everyone slept.

In the morning, we sat around my dining table and talked about
the relationship.

"I don't know what's happening," he said. "Or what this is."

"We've been exploring being more committed to each other,"
she said of him, to me. "And I think we're ready."

Then she inexplicably went out to buy bottled water, all of a sudden. He fucked me against the dining table, and said, "I need to be with you, not her."

She came back an hour later, we all breakfasted, and in two days they left for a vacation in Mexico. That was the end of the affair.

Kind of. There was more.

I had my own stuff to deal with, but as I came to see it, the problem with them as a duo was that they did not complement each other; they just seemed to thicken in each other's proximity. Once the cat-and-mouse was over, there was just this complicated heaviness to be dealt with.

I made the mistake of falling in love with him, and that scenario played itself out over several months, starting with lots of phone calls from Mexico and ending, inevitably, in their thick, abstruse togetherness, and my lone, flyaway, driven-to-distraction tears.

Licking my wounds, I didn't need to refer to the old saw "Why would you want to marry a man who cheats on his wife?" or even the more postmodern "Why would you want to marry a man who cheats on you *with* his wife?" The slap that woke me up was realizing that for all their esoteric, Dymaxion promise, Bob, Carol, Ted, and Alice are but the stray voluptuary's bourgeois bêtes made flesh, even now. I should not, in retrospect, have fallen asleep.

Freak Weather

"It's not you," he said. Strange what passes for comfort these days. There would be no tears or recriminations, apparently. We were going to pretend that no clandestine love affair had in fact occurred, that the past few months had been something on the order of a freak weather pattern. No tears, just a winded ache in the aftermath of so much passive destruction.

Three days later he left for Hawaii with his girlfriend.

The first night alone I drank a bottle of vodka, sitting on the living room floor and making tearful late-night phone calls to old friends. The next day, when my hangover cleared, at about four P.M., my friend Rob called and asked if I'd like to go to dinner at a restaurant called Mexico City. "Yes," I said, "but what I think I really need is to have some guy fuck me really hard. Maybe I should hire one of those people who advertise in the *L.A. X-Press.*" "That's an idea," Rob said. "I've done that a few times." One of the things I like about gay men is that, as a rule, they are willing to let sex be sex, rather than letting it become some kind of climatological algorithm. There are so many different kinds of sex, and our biggest lie is to pretend that sex is the Big Idea. I had just lost the man I loved to sexual terror. I didn't want to succumb to the affective undertow myself, drowning far out at sea under waves of sunny psychobabble, vodka and violence masquerading as apathy.

I went over to Rob's, and together we poured over the *X-Press* ads, looking for a guy for me. There weren't that many guys hidden among the ads for girls like "Valley Diva," "Barely Legal," and "Filipino Slut." Finally we stumbled on "Ebony Man," whose ad read simply, "Ladies, let me be your private dancer. All occasions."

I made Rob place the call. He explained to Ebony Man's voice pager that his pretty blond friend Hillary had just been dumped and needed company.

Next we called an ad that read, "Couples! Ladies! Men! Best massage, etc., by naked, horny, very muscular & handsome construction worker. I come to you." Same pager message.

The last ad we called was for "Women Only. Fun, smart, good looks blk male wants ladies 18–45, all races, all fantasy. 190, 6'3". Call Leon. 24 hrs. 9 in."

Only Leon called back. Rob put me on the phone. "Hi, Leon," I said. "I was too shy to call you myself. My boyfriend dumped me yesterday, and I want to see someone, but I don't want to go on a date." I wasn't sure whether I was feeling incredibly hostile or not. It seemed like a control-freak thing to do, wanting to pay some guy to do my bidding, but that seemed almost too simple, and it rang false. There's always hostility in sex, anyway, even when it serves merely to frame great tenderness, so that seemed hardly the point. I thought I felt very warm and simple about this encounter, in the sudden way disaster victims help each other.

Leon asked what I looked like, sounding polite but skeptical. "Blond," I said. "Five-seven, one thirty, blue eyes." He asked about my tits. "Thirty-four B," I said, and this seemed all right. "Are you a cop?" Leon asked, and I said no.

Once we established the fact that Rob would not be participating in any way, Leon agreed that meeting me at my house at midnight seemed fine. I said I'd page him when I got home.

"Don't you want to know anything about me?" he asked before hanging up.

I really didn't, but I said yes. He rattled off the same stats as were in the ad, adding that he had a good complexion and leaving off the "9 in." that had appeared in print at the tail end of his pitch, almost as an afterthought.

Rob and I ate seafood enchiladas, and on the way home, I thought about what I was doing. The idea of risk-taking occurred to me, a kind of moral bungee-jumping that makes one feel alive. I traveled across Brazil to Bolivia alone in 1988, and in the Brazilian border town of Corumbá I fell into a two-day conversation with an old American guy, a pilot.

"When you're in the air over the Bolivian jungle," he said, "you can see hundreds of airstrips. Many of them are abandoned, but you can't risk landing at them, because if they're run by smugglers, you'll be dead before the wheels even touch down. They'll get you with their AK-47's. Last year a bunch of biologists got it that way. They were on a research project." Whatever kind of work you do, it's important to be on speaking terms with danger; this is something I've always known. If you take no risks, all that will ever happen to you is that someday someone you love will be avoiding your eyes and saying, "It's not you."

As I drove down Vermont Avenue, back to Koreatown, I thought, *I have lived in Los Angeles for five years, I have never once taken a risk.*

I got home at eleven-thirty and paged Leon. "I'm coming from El Segundo," he said. "I'll be there in half an hour."

At midnight, the doorbell rang. I let Leon in, and he stood there in the middle of my yellow carpet, looking at me. I wondered what he saw. Because of the situation, by definition it could not be the same person anyone else had ever seen. That was the point.

Who was I? I looked around my apartment, wondering what kind of person I was. I looked past Leon at my red sofa. I have an obsession with sofas, I think they're horrible, and that they say the most intimate things about a person that can be said. I collect images of sofas from magazines, porno movies, back issues of *In Style*. I wondered what a guy like Leon would make of my red vinyl sofa bed. The first time I had sex with my newly ex-boyfriend, it had been on this sticky vinyl sofa, without either of us undressing or turning the light off in the curtainless room. As bad as that sofa was, that time is still sharply delineated in my fantasy life, somewhere between sense memory and imagination. I felt a twinge of regret, for a moment marveling hopelessly that something so good had inadvertently been worried to death in a vacuum, like a baby put in a clothes dryer by someone with Alzheimer's.

Leon stood there awkwardly in my living room. He looked a little stoned, maybe, though I'm not a good judge of these things. He seemed surprised that I was beautiful, and he was trying not to show it. "You're so pretty," he said.

He was a good-looking guy, with a shaved head, an unhappy smile, and hooded eyes, and no swagger. He was deferential without obsequiousness; he was role playing, acting the "submissive" only nominally, because he was as yet unsure what I wanted him to be. "Do you want me to sit down on the sofa?" he asked.

"Come on back to the bedroom."

We sat on the end of the bed. "Do you get a lot of calls?" I asked.

"N-no," he said with a visible effort at tactfulness. "Not a lot." It sounded as if he meant not any. He paused. "A lot of people call and hang up."

He looked at me sheepishly, as if I were the only woman in the world who'd ever hired a whore to soothe a broken heart. "What else do you do?" I asked. "For a living?"

"I paint houses," he said.

We kissed. Then we undressed, dryly and quickly. I felt very unromantic. I wanted this to be pornographic, just sex and inane chitchat. That's exactly what it was. He said I had a lovely ass. He was beautiful, more classically beautiful than suits my taste, muscular and proportionate, his arms still splattered with oil-based paint from the day's work. The paint splatters were what I liked best about him, because I felt, while he was touching me, that he was wearing a kind of fantasy costume.

Aside from the lack of any pretense, the sex wasn't qualitatively different from other sex I had had. It didn't fall outside the range of sexual experience in any way, except for the fact—which struck me as rather goofy, given the circumstances—that he did indeed have the largest organ I had ever seen. He was nice to me, and thorough, and an hour later we were lying side by side, and he asked me why I had called him.

"Oh, you know, getting back in the saddle after being thrown from the horse," I said. "Something to do with dignity." As I said this, it struck me as at least partly true. "And revenge, of course," I added as a joke.

"Revenge," he said. It made an impression on him. I was thinking he was simple, and he was thinking I was complex. None of that mattered, and that was what was nice about the situation.

I didn't have to pretend that it didn't matter, because it didn't.

After a few minutes, I wanted Leon to go, so I sat up and smiled and asked him how much. He stammered, and looked embarrassed, and stuttered when he finally spoke after several false starts, I meanwhile feeling incredulous and oddly touched. "F-f-f-forty-five?" he said hopefully. I gave him sixty, and that was that. He was gone by one A.M. and I was alone in my house, sitting on my red vinyl sofa, laughing, spent, and sore of heart.

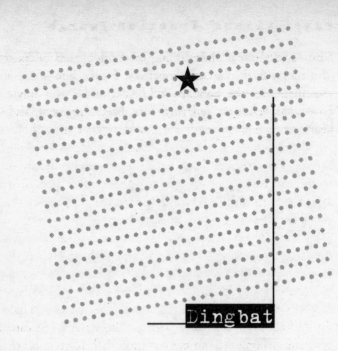

Dingbat

The food at Caffe Luna on Melrose isn't all that good, except for the *ravioli al funghi,* and the first glass of the house Chianti has that metallic wet-dog aftertaste until you get used to it, but I keep going because the L-shaped back patio, surrounded by latticework, trees, and twinkle lights, is one of the city's more pleasant places to loiter. Luna has the slowest service in all of Los Angeles, but it's slow in the European way, in that the assumption is that you'd naturally want to spend three or four hours over a meal, with lots of wine beforehand and an equal amount of coffee after, and it would be rude to present the check except after much pleading. And in a town that rolls up the sidewalks at ten P.M., Luna stays open until five in the morning. I've never gone there at that hour, but I feel safe knowing that I could.

But the main reason I come back to Caffe Luna again and again is Andrei the card reader, who has a knack for savvy, interpretive fortune-telling that makes him seem more like an inexpensive Gestalt therapist than a carny sideshow act.

Andrei isn't the only act at Luna; you can also buy roses, or have your handwriting analyzed by Steve, who got his start ten years ago, when he was living in a doorway across the street and needed to support his heroin habit, though since then he's cleaned up and has a rock-and-roll band. From two sentences and a signature, Steve promises to deduce personality, behavior patterns, and approximate IQ; the one time he did me, his summary pronouncement was, "You're ultra-abstract."

Andrei, however, belongs to a higher order of wandering minstrel. First of all, he looks like Lord Byron. He has the boyish locks, the pencil mustache, and the dark, dandyish rags of an L.A. hipster, but on him the look is more Oscar Wilde than Johnny Depp. Andrei is unusually tall, fair-skinned, and darkhaired, and he shuffles the Tarot deck with big hands at once capable and graceful, making erudite conversation with his regular clients before getting down to business with the cards.

The first time Andrei read my cards, the first question I put to him was "Is there life after death?" I'd been reading lots of popular physics books, and really wanted to know what the Tarot had to say on this interesting and insoluble question. As far as things like theoretical physics and the Tarot go, I am capable of believing and disbelieving many things at once. In fact, I'm most happy with a worldview that includes a healthy portion of the mutually exclusive, since the only times I've seriously erred were those in which I felt a strong sense of monodirectional conviction.

The cards confirmed my belief in an afterlife, so for my next question I asked if the guy I'd gone out with the week before was ever going to call me again. The answer there was no, which turned out to be absolutely correct, further reinforcing my belief in God and coincidentally cementing my faith in Andrei.

The second time I went for a reading, Andrei sat down at my table and said, "I was walking to work this afternoon, and I passed a basketball court where some kids were playing; a block later, I passed an old man crossing the street, and I thought, *Pain is the reason we die*. It's the effects of pain, that's all."

Which was exactly the kind of thing I needed to hear on that particular day. "And fear," I said. "The effects of fear."

A few months later, when I knew him better, I asked Andrei how he came to be a Tarot reader. "My mother introduced me to it," he said. "But I feel like I started really a long, long, long time ago. When I was two years old, my father found me in a restaurant and I'd approached a table and sat down with this old black sailor and was conversing with him on a philosophical level. I don't know if I made any predictions at that point in time, but I've always had that instinct to go and meet people I don't know and get right to the heart of things." He laughed. "That's kind of part of my genetic framework—to be intrusive."

So it was that when I started to get itchy feet, something that happens to me like clockwork every two years, I went straight to Caffe Luna for advice. Framing a question for a card reader is always a tricky project. I didn't want to tip my hand, or make my question too narrow. What I really wanted to know, I suppose, was something like "Am I doing the right thing with my life? Do I belong here? Should I get on a Greyhound bus and never look back? Am I ever going to fall in love again?" These are the questions that float around during the period when the two-year itch strikes. I thought long and hard while I held the deck of cards with its ornate gold pattern and finally said, "What's up with my living situation?"

Andrei laid out the cards, then singled out the Card of Sorrow. "There's a feeling surrounding the place where you live right now that isn't the best vibe. It's really been a vehicle for you up to a certain point, it's almost like a camper you've been living in, and you're ready to leave it." He looked at the cards again. "Before you leave it," he said, "you could really do some rituals to clean it out a little bit. You could burn some sage, give your house a rubdown of every corner."

He was right, of course. I'd had that bad-voodoo feeling about my apartment in Koreatown for some time. One day, when Janine came over to visit, she found a chicken bone on the windowsill in the hallway outside my front door. She grew agitated, and told me about a friend of hers who found a black velvet bag full of bones, cigar stubs, and candle ends under her nanny's bed. "And I've been hearing this a lot," Janine said, "about a cult of Guatemalan nannies in Beverly Hills who practice voodoo." I scoffed, and said that Tyrone's Guatemalan nanny was certainly not a witch; thereafter the phrase "Voodoo Nannies of Beverly Hills" became something of a running joke with us. But still, my house was somehow sour. Even my upstairs neighbor commented that no one had ever seemed happy in that apartment and the tenants always moved out, though I thought the problem was more likely the insidious noise of the industrial air conditioner on the roof of the minimall next door than an evil spirit.

"Is your place dark?" he asked.

I nodded ruefully. It was, in many ways, from the north-facing windows to the mysterious hole in the back of the spare-bedroom closet that led off into a black, infinite nowhere.

"The Six of Cups means that you need a lot more light."

"Lots more light," I said.

"When I saw the Three of Coins card I right away saw a house, a garden, space, simplistic furniture—kind of Zen in the sense of spaciousness and minimalism."

"Yes!" I said enthusiastically. By the time we finished the reading, I could see my new place: it would be modern, low-slung, and uncommonly clean. There would be carpeting, instead of the inevitable scuffed hardwood floors with dust devils under the furniture. And no grotty, overpainted moldings, or sticky doors. And lots of big, accessible closets with sliding-glass doors. Life would be goblin-free. And I wouldn't have to leave town to effect this miracle. Thank goodness Andrei hadn't said anything about adobe or skyscrapers!

I returned to my cold, clotted pasta with renewed hope.

Andrei rose to leave, then paused and said thoughtfully, "It's that you have become on some level almost addicted to the un-resolvable complexity of things. A part of you wants to have a normal life, and the question is, How can you go there?"

I was tempted to shoot back a "You can't get there from here" reply, but I held my tongue. It's impossible to be cynical with Andrei.

A couple of months later, I had gathered enough momentum to start looking for apartments. Rob, who like me is prone to thinking about his inner self as having a floor plan rather than an anatomy, came along for the ride. We spent lazy Sundays doing the *New York Times* crossword puzzle over coffee and leftover pasta, then taking long, meandering drives around likely parts of town, looking out for buildings with "For Rent" signs.

For a while, we fell in love with a building in the foothills near Runyon Canyon called the Del Prado. The Del Prado is a fifties-modern dreamscape, a long, low building surrounded by succulent dark foliage. We sneaked in for a look behind a woman in white go-go boots walking a pit bull, and entered a cool, leafy courtyard, where giant, sinister philodendrons, stands of bamboo, and spreading palms harbored surprising little gazebos, statuary, and a bird's-egg-blue pool. Through the ubiquitous sliding-glass doors, we could see into everyone's apartments, and the tenants seemed to run to artist types: faux marble-painted walls covered in arcane primitive artworks, rooms papered in abstract expressionist paint-ings, glass-bead curtains, walls of books. I wanted these people to invite me to their dinner parties. And I wanted to have brunch on Sundays by the pool.

A trim Vietnamese woman showed us the apartment that was available, a two-bedroom in one of the darker recesses of the building. For a good twenty minutes I walked in and out of rooms, wanting so very much to love it, but there, sadly, were all the things I'd sworn off: the battered, uneven hardwood floors, the gummy, overpainted woodwork in the inconvenient little kitchen, high rent, and worst of all, windows in the back looking onto a cinder-block wall. Rob kept eyeing me, biting his tongue, though he knew it was all wrong. Eventually, I sighed, shook my head, and we moved on.

The next place we fell in love with was a fourteen-story high-rise building on Whitley Drive, between Franklin and Hollywood Boulevard, ideally situated within walking distance of Musso & Frank Grill, where one would dearly love to imbibe martinis and eat steak and Caesar salad on a regular basis. The place was built in 1966 and hasn't been changed in the least detail since then; it's a swinger's paradise, with boxy blue-and-orange ceramic-tile ornamentation all over the outside, so that the building from afar looks like an oversized trailer-park Mondrian knockoff. Inside, huge sixties grotesque plastery podlike chandelier things hung over a swath of deep carpet in the lobby, where a uniformed desk clerk buzzes in guests. He called a woman from the rental office for us, a dark, middle-aged woman who was made up like a wedding cake and said her name was Cher.

Cher showed us a "one-bedroom with den" on a low floor, facing north. The bar in the kitchen was perfect for a set of chrome-and-vinyl stools, while the living room cried out for a velveteen sectional sofa and a mirrored coffee table such as you'd have if you were inclined to cut up lines of cocaine. The living room and den area were separated by a retractable pleated vinyl "wall" that I instantly fell in love with. "It's so louche," Rob said, "I love that word, louche."

"Yes, love it!" I said. I could see myself here, in my Pierre Cardin three-piece men's suit with the flared trousers, and my white patent leather loafers. Maybe some gold Chanel chains around my neck.

Cher showed us the laundry facilities and the kidney-shaped pool on the mezzanine, and we were very, very tempted, though we didn't much like the sign at the pool that said "No Guests on Sundays." Ultimately, we decided that living in a Scorsese movie would not be desirable on a long-term basis, and we passed.

A few days later we found my ideal building, on a quiet street in Los Feliz. It was again a split-level complex around a pool, which seemed to be our layout of preference. This one was built in the forties, so it was more modern than the fifties Del Prado—which had traces of that passing colonial yearning that haunts apartments of that era—and more serious and clean than the trippy sixties high-rise. We rang the manager and jumped up and down in place while we waited for her.

She liked us on sight, and led us to a graceful apartment with high, slanted, beamed ceilings and walls of glass. Every detail, from the Formica on the counters to the conical light fixtures, was pristine and original. I started to get a buzzy, euphoric feeling at the top of my head; it flushed down to the tips of my fingers, and I knew I was in love.

I opened the louvered door that led to the patio, and got the first sign that something was seriously amiss with this situation. "Watch out! The surface is very fragile!" She looked at my loafers and shook her head. "You have to take your shoes off, if you want to walk around out there." Suddenly she dove past me and fell to her hands and knees, where she started picking up tiny bits of something. "The building has a gravel roof," she said, "and pieces of it blow off in the wind and land here. You'll have to collect them and give them back to me." Rob and I exchanged a meaningful look. I said something about it being a nice place for plants and such. "Oh!" the landlady said in a peculiar tone. "You can't have plants here!"

Neither, it turned out, could you have children, not really, nor guests. "You can't take children in the pool," she said brusquely when I mentioned Tyrone's existence. "And can't have guests in the pool, no more than one guest per week, and then you have to be in it with them. That's the rules, and I'm very strict, ask anyone in the building."

Come to think of it, we hadn't seen a living soul on the premises. As we left the apartment I felt an acute pang of regret for the love that could never be, certain as I was at that moment that there would never, ever be another apartment like this one.

On the way out, I noted that the building next door had a "For Rent" sign, but at that point Rob and I were both too low to pursue it. I did scribble down the phone number on the back of an envelope, and called that night just for good measure. The next day I glumly drove over to look at it, only because it was unbelievably cheap.

And that is how I found my apartment, which turned out to be no architectural wonder but a noble beast nonetheless—a species of thing called the dingbat.

After five years of living in Los Angeles, I know I'm beginning to assimilate. How can I tell? Because I've finally moved into a dingbat. A dingbat is one of those chicken-wire-and-stucco apartment buildings—you know the type: two stories, with the carports in the back, some kind of fanciful, theme-park façade, and a permanent "Now Renting" sign staked in the little island of shrubbery out front. Dingbat apartments are the kind bachelors and bachelorettes came in and out of on *Love, American Style.* (Living in them leaves you prone to use TV-inspired references, since they usually come with basic cable.)

This is the thing everyone fears will happen to them if they move here: that they'll come to live in this very apartment. I kid you not. It's a valid concern.

Dingbats look like motels, and in some sense, they are. The very motelness of the new apartment was what finally, after so much fanciful flannery, drew me in—the brilliant solution to the two-year itch was to move into a place that captured the essence of the temporary. Rather than hauling great heaps of musty books and tattered furniture from one ancient hovel to another every couple of years, I would settle light as a polyester feather into sparse plastic surroundings with all the hominess of an airport departure lounge. I'm not being the least bit ironic. This was the perfect way to create some kind of faux momentum in my frighteningly sedentary life.

My new living room has brown, deep-pile carpet, a whole wall done in mirror and tan fake brick, a cottage-cheese ceiling, and vertical blinds. The only furnishings are a brown boomerang sofa, the white Formica Saarinen coffee table I bought on the street for twenty bucks, a Lucite swag lamp, and a thrift-store painting of a matador. It's very easy to clean. The whole apartment is that way: it's like living in a self-cleaning oven.

Every morning, I put on my dark glasses, open my sliding glass door, and take my instant coffee out by the pool. I feel pleasantly anonymous. I could be anyone, I could be anywhere. I could be going somewhere, or nowhere. Best of all, I could be going nowhere on purpose; nowhere could just be my *aesthetic.*

I learned to appreciate the dingbat by reading Reyner Banham's *Los Angeles: The Architecture of Four Ecologies,* a book that left me with a permanent fondness for freeway overpasses. Banham was a British professor of architectural history, and his 1971 "rearview mirror" view of L.A.'s architectural history is as absorbing and culturally seminal as Raymond Chandler's *The Big Sleep* or Mike Davis's *City of Quartz.*

Banham says things like this: "Los Angeles is the Middle West raised to flash-point, the authoritarian dogmas of the Bible Belt and the perennial revolt against them colliding at critical mass under the palm trees. Out of it comes a cultural situation where only the extreme is normal, and the Middle Way is just the unused reservation down the centre of the Freeway."

Statements like this, so alarmingly well put, hint at how the British have always gotten away with so much cultural weirdness— they explain it all so beautifully, you'd let them get away with just about anything. Hearing Banham perform this exegetic service on behalf of Los Angeles, one can't help but be moved, and what's more, one begins to feel the stirrings of a teleologically viable civic sense. Los Angeles begins to feel like a real place, with a living, breathing, feeling persona.

I have always aspired in my heart to the architecture of Richard Neutra and Rudolph Schindler, or at least a Case Study house filled with furniture from Herman Miller and Knoll. If L.A. has a soul, an essence, with any purity, it's in that native genre of mod-

ern architecture. Nothing, to me, is more appalling than the idea
of a nice little craftsman bungalow, one of those site-dyspeptic
little farmhouses scattered all over town, or those Spanish-colonial-
revival duplexes that always seem to be in the middle of a great
residential nowhere, wherever they are. For a while, I also had a
similar dread of dingbats—without knowing that was what they
were called. That was until I learned to see them through the
Banhamian lens, through which they are transformed. No more
mean hovels—instead, "the unadorned rear elevations of dingbats
in Freewayland often have a Schindlerian air about their simple
assembly of flat stucco planes."

It's true! Now I'm a convert: I look around my boxy, low-slung
pad, and where once I might have seen cheapness, I see only
streamlined efficiency, ease of living, a low-budget paradise that
embodies the best of everything Bucky Fuller was aiming for in
the 1930s when he designed his Dymaxion House.

Banham even dotes on the dingbat's wonky ornamental façade,
which he calls "a statement about the culture of individualism,"
enumerating the variety of styles in loving detail: "Everything is
there from Tacoburger Aztec to Wavy-line Moderne, from Cod
Cape Cod to unsupported Jaoul vaults, from Gourmet Mansardic
to Polynesian Gabled and even—in extremity—Modern Architecture."

My dingbat's façade is more like the latter, a kind of Gonzo-
Corbu, with long, thin wraparound windows and these white
things I can only call vertical elements. If you haven't read Banham, you wouldn't like it. You'd probably prefer my old place, in
Koreatown, the one with "Old World charm," as the want ads
say, but then, there you go—one person's nightmare is another
person's California Dream.

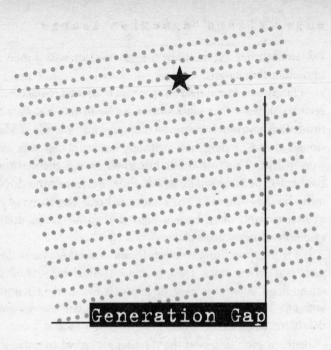

Generation Gap

What was the first rock concert you ever went to?" Nancy asked me as we waited in line at the Great Western Forum to see Nine Inch Nails and David Bowie.

I winced. "Peter Frampton."

Nancy nodded sagely. "*Frampton Comes Alive.*"

"No, wait," I said suddenly, "I lied. It was K. C. and the Sunshine Band!"

Neither of us had been to an arena concert since she was fifteen, which was more than fifteen years ago for each of us. We were drawn by fear and curiosity and not a little morbidity. Bowie was hugely responsible for my fashion sense at a tender age, though I'm a fickle and neglectful fan—the kind who's likely to run away for months at a time with the Glen Miller Orchestra, or spend a season at the opera.

I knew nothing about Nine Inch Nails beyond the bit of tape

I'd heard in the car on the way to the forum, and that had left no particular impression.

"Don't you remember your parents wearing grown-up clothes?" Nancy asked as we pushed through the crowd. She said this as a thirty-five-year-old mother wearing Levi's, a baby-doll T, and clogs.

"Actually, no," I said. My mom had been a sixties babe in her youth, and a late-blooming hippie in the seventies. She'd never really gotten around to grown-up clothes. I remember mostly the year when she made herself a giant wool Sherlock Holmes coat and wore it everywhere, to my teenage chagrin.

I was wearing a T-shirt, jeans, and Converse high-tops, an allusion to the days when you waited outside a concert for hours to get in, and dressed with a siege mentality. For Frampton, I remember, I wore jeans and Jack Purcell sneakers, and a red-white-and-blue tube top to which I'd pinned an awful red-crepe flower. During the concert, the flower bled red dye all over my chest.

Nancy and I had assigned seats, and we found them without incident. A band was playing onstage while people filed in—a thankless gig if ever there was one, the basketball stadium flooded with fluorescent lights, and no hint of applause—except from Nancy.

"Didn't think they'd sound like that," she said, when the band finished and started knocking down equipment.

"That's not Nine Inch Nails," I said.

Nancy stopped whistling and clapping and said, "I was wondering."

When Trent Reznor came on, he made no particular impression on me, either. As he flipped his rocker hair up and down, writhed soulfully, and threw his mike stand in the air, I didn't feel moved, but neither did I feel culturally dislocated: no, I felt like I could have been watching Alice Cooper. Or Aerosmith. Or Spinal Tap.

However much I squinted, I could see nothing but parodic rock-and-roll clichés, though I knew I was probably wrong. Scott loves Trent Reznor and once compared him to Mussorgsky. About halfway through the set, Nancy and I looked at each other, shrugged, and headed out to the concourse for a Coke. We weren't the only ones.

The concourse was far from deserted: pale teenage girls in cut-offs and Doc Martens, a twentyish couple in high *Mod Squad* with their high dudgeon attitudes, a Stevie Nicks type in a velvet cape, a middle-aged man in a top hat and whiteface, four Latino boys handsome in zoot suits, three thirty-five-year-old women from the secretarial pool in pantyhose and sensible shoes. The whole postmordial stewpot loitering around the concourse, scuffing up the linoleum.

Everyone looked lost. What was missing from this equation was the mad, orgiastic crush of twenty thousand fifteen-year-olds united in epiphany. There was no generational phenomenon occurring here, no youth culture at all—and that left nothing but a lot of loud, muddy music, bad sightlines, and rude ushers.

We made our way back to our seats. Waiting for Bowie to appear, I was suddenly afraid that he would make me feel like a dinosaur, that he would limp cynically into the spotlight and do his best to whip a bunch of arthritic glamourpusses into a mild frenzy. He didn't at all. Onstage he moved like an adult, very calm and assured and talented, without a trace of camp or hoar. Which meant that as an arena concert it was a catastrophe, if for the noblest of reasons.

It struck me later, watching the little postmodern pods of people drain out of the Forum long before the concert had finished, that what has died may be something broader than rock and roll: the whole idea of the "generation gap" seemed to be vanishing before my eyes.

"Nancy," I said in the car, "are we old or young or what?"

"I don't know, baby," she said in the voice she usually uses for her child, "I don't know."

☆

A few months later, Anne called me up to see if I wanted to drive down to Costa Mesa with her for a Persian disco party. "I can't promise you anything," she said. "It's Persians, and they said to dress up."

The day of the party, we talked on the phone, strategizing wardrobe, supposing that we might well be the only Caucasians, and trying to figure out how to look really fab without also invoking our usual tongue-in-cheek blonde-brunette-combo hooker effect, just in case there were older, shockable, or excitable Persians at the party. We met at my house and tried on several outfits each, arriving at a black Betsey Johnson strapless sheath and clear Lucite platform sandals for Anne, and a high-necked but clingy gold vintage dress for me. As we went out the door, I ran back to grab my holey Levi's jacket, thinking mainly that if the car broke down on the freeway and one of us needed to walk to the call box, it would be best to have some camouflage in the car.

When we pulled up to the Costa Mesa Ramada Inn, where the party was, the first thing we saw was a group of a half-dozen Persian youths in crisp-pressed khakis and polo shirts. They looked to be in high school—junior college, tops. As we rounded the building to the parking lot, we saw more of the same, and I gripped Anne's arm. "Anne," I said levelly, "they're all young, they're all boys, and we're dressed like hookers."

We parked the car in a dark corner, and Anne changed her dress, while I wrapped myself in my denim jacket and took my hair down, both of us cursing and giggling. Sufficiently modified, we tottered on into the hotel, through the lobby, and down an escalator to the ballroom level. There before us was a swarm of a couple hundred young Persian glitterati, at least half of them female, waiting to get into the packed party.

Anne's friend spotted us right away—we were, in fact, the only Caucasians—and led us to a place in line. He'd brought his roommate; both of them were perfumey with clean laundry and youthful beauty and eagerness—quite overwhelming to me in my scratchy gold dress, sticky makeup, and excessive years—and the foursome quickly turned into an awkward double-date affair with everyone saying things like, "How was the drive?" and "I've heard a lot about you."

I took the long, awkward silences to look around the crowd, and it was a stunning sight: they were the most beautiful, handsome, well-dressed, attractive bunch of people I had ever seen assembled in one place. They made the Oscar-night party crowds I'd written up for the L.A. Times look like a bunch of nerdy, aging drag queens and fatuous gigolos. The boys were all studiedly casual and pristine, their hair brilliantly, subtly coiffed, their shoes natty. And the girls—there were lithe club girls in vinyl minis and boots, busty vixens in bell-bottomed black unitards, Chanel-suited cuties with shiny buttons and perfect hair. Every one of them carried a designer purse from South Coast Plaza, something strappy, cute, and brand-label chic. Suddenly my dear Prada handbag looked like a flea-bitten old sack, which is something I had never felt even in the rest room of the Four Seasons Hotel, when I dried my hands on linen napkins cheek by jowl with the Beverly Hills Ladies Who Lunch and reached into its quilted mouth for my lipstick.

I was at once charmed and humiliated. We waited for a long time, being introduced to various handsome young men who politely said hello and didn't talk to us, nor did we talk to them. "Stunning," I whispered to Anne, and she said, "They're gorgeous!"

When we got inside, the party was like a supercool prom night, laser lights making patterns on the walls, big round tables ringing a dance floor where couples danced while the Persian disco music pulsed. We lost the boys immediately, then went to the bar, got a couple of the nonalcoholic drinks, and stood around in a state of fascination and great psychic pain. The boys came back periodically to find us, and we duly shooed them away, admonishing them to pick up girls and have some fun, don't mind us. "Come dance," they said, "we'll teach you Persian dancing."

Neither of us felt equal to the task. It was all mildly embarrassing and weary. After a while, Anne and I found ourselves a vantage point and sat down, watching the dancers, who were intent on their fabulous moves, which involved a shimmying and twisting of the hips and wrists in synch. Then the music turned suddenly to American disco, something hideous like Gloria Gaynor. Everyone visibly blanched, but went at it with game vigor once the shock had passed. When Kool and the Gang came on, Anne and I found a space and danced ourselves, even though the whole time I felt outside myself, just the way you don't want to feel when you dance. I'm a bad dancer—I'm a good dancer when I'm in the mood, which is rare, and almost always at gay clubs, where there's an ecstatic glee you can catch and ride—but ordinarily, when dancing situations arise, I'm lethargic, and uncreative, and my body feels like a big cardboard box. At best I imitate the dopey moves of someone on *American Bandstand*.

So we danced, then we sat, then we wandered. Pretty soon the boys found us again, and we tried to talk, everyone shouting *"What?"* over the music. They took us outside, into the lobby. "You're bored!" they said, and we protested. "No, you're bored. It's a terrible party. We know it's a terrible party. It was supposed to be very different. Lots of things went wrong."

No, we said, there are lots of cute girls, you should go back in.

"We could get a hotel room and some booze," the roommate said halfheartedly, the first time I've ever heard anyone say that just to be nice.

No, we said, that's okay, really. Go back to the party.

They ended up sitting with us in the closed bar upstairs until the party ended. Anne's friend demonstrated karate moves, though I think he was making it up. At two A.M. they said, "Come, we'll go eat now. No, you must come, it's just down the street."

So we went down the street to a Persian restaurant, where there was a huge crowd of all sorts of Persians, young and old, all of them wide awake at this odd hour. A gray-bearded guy in a polyester suit was singing Persian love songs, while another guy played synthesizer: Persian lounge lizards.

The roommate leaned over and said, "I hate him." He made a face. "I just hate him!"

"The Persian Bill Murray?" I said, but I think he was too young to know who Bill Murray was.

Some people from the party were already seated at a long table, and after discussion with the waiter, we pulled up another table to the end and sat down. None of the people at the rest of the table looked at us.

Anne's friend ordered us yogurt sodas, just to see us grimace. I actually didn't mind it so much, though they took my actually drinking the stuff as discomfort at their humor, and grew suddenly, dismayingly solicitous.

The roommate and I made polite conversation. The possibility of me sleeping with him had been amply discussed at various times between Anne and her friend, between Anne and me, and I'd guess between the roommates themselves, but we didn't talk about it, and it certainly wasn't going to happen now, if ever. By now I was bone-tired and achy from awkwardness. We begged off on a last, feeble invite to "go to our friend's house and shoot some pool," and left them in the restaurant at half past three in the morning.

Anne dropped me off at about four. "Remember in New York," she said ruefully, "the bars closed at four, it was nothing."

"You're right," I said. "It's all very strange."

I woke up at seven, drank some NyQuil, and went back to bed until noon. We hadn't had a drop of alcohol, but all day I felt like I had a hangover. Anne called in the evening and said, "I'm so sorry, I owe you one, will you ever forgive me?" I laughed.

"Those girls were so beautiful," Anne said.

And I said, "We weren't so bad. Did you see how they wouldn't look at us?"

"I know, but they're young, and hip, and enticing."

"Yes," I said, "for now. They're amazing now, and in a couple of years, they'll land a husband, and they'll be elegant matrons.

Unlike us, who are basically the same as we were at twenty. I mean basically. We're still cute, and we still disco."

Anne groaned. She had a false hangover, too. "You're right," she said. "We're insane."

"I'm glad to be home," I said. "It was like being in one of those *Star Trek* episodes where the crew ages a year a minute, and then just before they die of rickets or something, Dr. McCoy gives them a shot and they reverse-age in seconds. That's what happened to us last night."

"What does it mean?" Anne asked.

"I think it means we can never leave Los Angeles."

"I have a headache," Anne said, "I'm going to take a nap."

We hung up the phone and each drifted off to sleep in Never Never Dreamland, a landscape where there is no horizon, just a collectively hallucinated oasis, an imagined horizon line with palm trees and water that always seems to be just a little bit farther, then a little bit farther, and then again a little bit farther away.

Pizza Boys

It was my thirty-third birthday, and I didn't do anything, because I had a deadline the next day that was giving me cold sweats, and I didn't think I'd be good company. It took me a long time to remember what I'd done on my thirty-second birthday—it always does. I repress birthdays the way I throw unopened bank statements into a drawer. Only interest makes you old. But I finally did remember my thirty-second, once I stopped trying so hard: my friend Corinne organized Sunday dinner of fried chicken and mashed potatoes at a south L.A. place called Maurice's Snack 'N Chat, to which she invited a breathtaking array of unattached men, including a Creole ballet dancer from New Orleans, a diminutive rare-book collector, and a great big cowboy from Montana named Howdy. Corinne is one of those enviable girls who wears overalls and miniskirts the same way and reads more, better books than I do and writes dense, intelligent

fiction *just for fun* and sleeps with interesting men less interesting than she is, and makes her living, improbably, as a sitcom
actress. The birthday party, in retrospect, was cast like an ensemble sitcom and played brilliantly. Everyone got on famously and
Corinne ended up doing the two-step with the Creole ballet dancer
in the middle of Pico Boulevard. I didn't dance, but I did get a
lava lamp from my editor-in-chief and his girlfriend, who found
the evening very curious and never, to their credit, asked for an
explanation.

I purposely skipped my thirty-third birthday entirely, though the
next weekend a sort-of postbirthday party began to crystallize
around the idea of a bunch of us getting together at my shag-
carpet palace to watch *Showgirls* and then the premiere episode
of an execrable softcore porno thing Nancy had written for cable.
For no good reason, it ended up being an all-girl party. Must have
been the porn aspect—something about porn that makes for unconscious wagon-circling gender behavior. Seems naughtier that
way.

I got Tyrone down to bed by eight-thirty, and did my hair up
in a Bond-girl do with a tall, silly ponytail, then put on blue eye
shadow and a hot pink polyester floor-length hostess dress.

Anne came, bringing me a leopard-print scarf from her vacation
in Barcelona. Janine came, bringing me a Dean Martin CD, which
she said went with my new apartment. Nancy brought a cheese-
cake, saying, "I thought it appropriate to the evening's theme."
She also brought Lauren, her friend from New York who'd just
moved to L.A. and was writing soap operas.

Before the movie started, Nancy pulled me aside and took a
piece of paper out of her purse. "I have to show you something.
It's an invitation to the producer's birthday party." She meant the
producer of the softcore porn series, which was another all-girl
affair.

I read the paper with mounting horror. It was an invitation to
an all-girl sweat lodge in Topanga Canyon, actually what looked

like an all-Jewish-girl sweat lodge. "It's appalling," I said. "You have to go, even if it's just to perv on it!" "Yeah," Nancy said, "I guess I should go."

Lori walked in last, with two pizzas and margarita fixings. She sat down and for the next hour squeezed limes and crushed ice with dogged zeal, as if she were breaking rocks in a quarry, while we all looked on from the corners of our eyes with mounting awe. She'd just spent the summer taking her boyfriend's five kids to one waterpark after another, and clearly hadn't come down from it yet. Still, she was the only one among us with a real boyfriend, and a darned good one at that. Well, except for Lauren, who was married. I didn't know Lauren, but she was apparently married in an undiluted, East Coast sense.

"You know," I said, turning to Anne and Janine, "I never thought about it quite this way, but I just realized that both of you are dating pizza delivery boys."

"What," Anne said, turning to Janine, "not you too?"

Janine gave a Cheshire Cat grin and nodded.

Unlikely, yes, but there you have it: two of my friends are dating pizza delivery boys.

Janine's is a struggling actor. I've never met him, but I picture a Ron Goldman/Tom Cruise type in chinos, polo shirt, and sporty sunglasses. This is probably inaccurate, it's just that I want to imagine him as an upscale delivery boy who takes tiny expensive artichoke, goat cheese, and prosciutto pizzas to mansions in Brentwood and Bel Air, wanting to be invited in, hoping to be discovered. He's twenty-four and Janine is thirty-two.

Anne's pizza boy is a twenty-two-year-old chiropractic student who lives with his parents in Rancho Cucamonga. She met him on the freeway, during a heavy-traffic slowdown, when he tied his phone number to a heavy object and tossed it through her open car window. Anne looks about nineteen, or at least if she told you she was nineteen you wouldn't seriously doubt her, but she's really thirty-nine.

This chiropractic student I have met. He's got that blush of youth about him, all springy and tender and strapping, a man-boy like you only dream of. Rancho Cucamonga is a dire, pseudo-Tudor bedroom community where the only kind of pizza he could possibly be delivering would be the big, bland, soggy two-for-one-and-free-Pepsi kind with Canadian bacon and pineapple, or pepperoni and black olives.

"I asked him, once, if he ever got lucky on his rounds—you know, with the lonely housewives and the California King master suites, and the like," said Anne.

Lori looked up from her lime-squeezing. "What did he say?"

"He said yeah, sure, sometimes."

"How?" Janine asked. "How do they approach it, I mean, what do they *say?*"

"Different things," Anne said. "One woman just took a look at him and dropped her blouse right there in the doorway. But the line that always worked on him, and always meant one thing, was when they said, 'Want a slice?' "

We fell out howling. " 'Want a slice?' " I repeated, trying out the line. " '*Want* a slice?' 'Want a *slice?*' It's impossible!"

We watched *Showgirls* with heavy heckling.

"Look!" Anne said. "They're skipping. They're actually skipping arm in arm."

"That's what girls do when they bond," I said.

Halfway through the movie, Lori finished making the drinks. By the time Nancy's show came on, I was headachy from the movie, the sweet drinks were too little too late, and I had no élan left. The show's opener came on, and a breathy, Kewpie doll voice said, "Next, written by women, directed by women . . ."

"Sounds like a douche commercial," Nancy snorted.

For the next half hour she winced and frowned as her campy, dirty little script about a group of science students who built an orgasm machine revealed itself on-screen as a smooshy, soft-focus, marshmallow pie.

"I didn't write that shower scene!" she said bitterly toward the beginning, then lapsed into appalled silence. I kibitzed a little at first, though no one else there knew whether to be saying nice things or laughing or crying, so they kept quiet. It only lasted half an hour, and after that things picked up again and we kept on until one in the morning.

For days after the party, I couldn't get the pizza-boy concept off my mind. The more I thought about it, the more I saw that what I wanted wasn't a husband or a real boyfriend, just a nice pizza delivery boy, that was the ticket. I wasn't in the cocktail-party mood, hadn't been for months now, and all the possible sex partners you meet at those things are cynical twits anyway, nothing but New Age boffins, jaundiced professional know-it-alls, and the callow middle-aged.

Time and again I've heard friends say, "Men in L.A. are intimidated by smart, interesting women." I don't think this is really it; I think it's more an evolutionary phenomenon. The truth is, L.A. has never been populated by means of reproduction. People come here from somewhere else, at a certain viable age, a steady stream of them for as long as the city can remember. There is no longer any real reason to mate once you get to L.A. and that's why sex is such a drag. Once the hormones settle down, along about the age of twenty-two, twenty-four, guys here lose their rutting edge and start acting like puzzled, oversocialized schoolgirls. Women in their thirties need to know this.

Eventually, a plan began to form in my wee brain. It was all so simple, I thought, cackling: the best way to meet young, unspoiled, refreshing types would be to start ordering lots of pizzas!

I'd ordered pizzas before, of course, but always for Tyrone when I was too tired to cook, and pizza delivery with a cranky four-year-old in the background has never been terribly titillating. But I had a dim recollection that the guys who brought the pizzas were collectively cute. Almost all young men are reasonably attractive when they're twenty-two, if they're fit enough to bound up and down apartment stairs all night carrying pizzas.

Then, as I thought about it more, what seemed so simple began to seem rather more complicated. There was, first off, the huge risk of coming off as a pathetic, lonely nutball, a lurid vision of stretch marks in a negligee. What did you wear to order pizza? Clearly nothing overtly sexy; but then again, you didn't want something too binding, either. The episode had to be fairly spontaneous, and you didn't want to be forever getting out of your jeans. And what were you supposed to be doing, that you would order a whole pizza up when you were home alone for the evening? Watching television? Too pathetic. Working, maybe: it was true that you could see my computer screen from the front door, and I could stick a pencil behind my ear before I went to the door, though that might be dangerous.

Maybe better to stick with the lonely-housewife persona. One of my best, long-running fantasies involves a TV repairman and a lonely housewife. Sometimes I'm the housewife, and sometimes I'm the repairman—actually, there are always two repairmen, but one is bald and fat and only watches. I don't know why this pedestrian fantasy appeals to me, but it always works. So housewife would be fine, or at least there was no sound reason for concocting any other manifest identity.

For a couple of weeks I mulled over the project without getting up the energy or the nerve to try it out. I told Rob what I had in mind, and he said, "My God, Hillary, it's a fine idea, but I can't imagine you actually *saying* that. 'Wanna slice?' Are you serious?" He laughed heartily. "I could say it," I protested. "Really I could."

Then one evening when I happened to be home alone and at loose ends, I got tired of thinking about it, dialed up Little Caesar's, and ordered a small mushroom pizza. Little Caesar was Tyrone's favorite, and I remembered distinctly that the day I moved in, a tall, breathtakingly beautiful guy came, followed immediately by a cute cable guy and a pair of refrigerator delivery men who came repellently close to my fantasy TV repairman duo (the point of true fantasy being always that it's something you wouldn't actually want to do). Every so often I ordered Little Caesar's for Tyrone, and sometimes it was the cute guy, other times another, older, lumpish one, so I figured I had a fifty-fifty chance, and that

I'd be relieved, anyway, if it turned out to be Lumpy, in which case I could give up and say I tried.

Forty minutes later, my doorbell rang. I opened the door, and there he was, the same guy, tall, cute, and gawky. I gestured for him to step in and put the pizza on the coffee table. "How much?" I asked, and stood by the couch, rummaging through my purse.

He said a price, and I rummaged some more.

"Where's your little boy?" he asked.

I looked at him. "He's staying at his father's tonight," I said. He nodded. I made a weak gesture in the direction of my desk. "Working late," I said. I laughed. "I guess you are, too."

He laughed politely. The air in the room seemed to get a little thick right then, in that man-and-woman-alone-in-a-room way. It could have been my imagination, but those things usually aren't, and though it wasn't overpowering, some slight frisson was definitely there, even if it was a bit forced.

Then it struck me, what a silly nitwit I was being, and I gave him his money and smiled briskly, opening the screen door. "Thanks," I said.

I closed the door, thanking my lucky stars for my narrow escape. It took me ten minutes to realize I'd forgotten to give him a tip.

Some time later, Nancy called me. "Remember that women's sweat lodge?" she said, sounding angry. "Well, I'm *not* going. I talked to Tim"—her ex, who is a Native American—"and he said, 'Nancy, this is serious stuff. You can't just play around with it like it's some fluff.' And I realized he was absolutely right."

I hung up the phone, feeling mortified, and relieved, for Nancy and her women and me and my pizza boy. Never again, I resolved, would I have anything to do with an all-girl party.

O, Prada Handbag!

Beverly is a woman of a certain age, which is to say, much younger or older than she looks, or both. She is even vague about how long she has been a woman. Her face is well lined, her cheekbones high, her complexion somewhat rugged. Her hair could be blond or gray, but let's call it platinum. She's trim, though she doesn't flaunt it, except for a bangled forearm, and her long, exquisite legs, legs which have never straddled a Lifecycle or mounted a StairMaster; Bev's acerbic personality alone has a thermogenically slimming effect. She's sharp, though not necessarily intelligent—or rather, her intelligence is neither intellectual nor emotional, but taxonomic: she is a creature of style and society.

Her best friends are Joan Collins and Princess Di, two most civilized and accomplished women, either of whom it is strangely easy to picture hunkering down over a joint of fresh kill in a cave somewhere. The soupçon of brutality is what gives these women's stylishness a contrapuntal authenticity.

Bev shops, she lunches, she sits on benefit committees, she deals
in real estate. She has had either four husbands—all of them fol-
lies—or just the one forever and ever, he fat, balding, and away
on business. Either way, she's patently asexual. She has two adult
children, one on Lithium and the other leading some kind of pedestrian middle-class life in Orange County. Coquette, courtesan,
Beverly is a true demimondaine, a direct descendant of Colette's
Gigi.

"Where she came from in France is anyone's guess. She said
one thing one day and another thing the next. She was a peasant—
and a genius. Peasants and geniuses are the only people who
count, and she was both." That's Diana Vreeland describing Coco
Chanel, but substitute Middle America for France, and she could
just as well have been speaking of the Lady Beverly Hills.

I got to know Beverly Hills only very recently.

It all began the day I scored a Prada handbag at my neighborhood Goodwill store. The purchase threw me into a state of al-
tered fashion consciousness, and nothing has ever been the same
since.

Thrift-shopping in L.A., if you're persistent and discerning,
yields much more than vintage party frocks and goofy sixties pant
suits, and many times before I had come away with treasures—a
leopard-print Diane von Furstenburg wrap dress from, I believe,
1976; an Adolfo gown; Ferragamo pumps; a men's Brooks Brothers tuxedo that fits me like a glove; a pair of Chanel earrings. But
that handbag was a different order of discovery, a coveted object
of Grail-like significance and magnitude. Nothing can describe the
tremendous rush of desire I felt upon first seizing hold of the
braided gold-and-leather shoulder strap and feeling the black
quilted bag nestle at my side: the perfect length, the perfect size,
the perfect weight. The corners were slightly frayed, but nothing
that a black Magic Marker wouldn't fix, and such a minor flaw
was barely a consideration, given the 2,500 percent markdown.

The Prada handbag proved to be an ideal marriage of beauty

and function, and our union became equally perfect, as my purse and I instantly achieved that synergistic coupling by which the parts are made greater than the whole, a dynamic made more catholic by the mysterious aura of luxe attached to our great Italian surname. "O, Prada handbag!" became the "O, sole mio!" of my heart.

I was spoiled, instantly and forever. Thus it was that when I found myself shuffling back and forth to Naturemart and the video store in a pair of worn-out flip-flops, I resolved to skip the mall and head for Rodeo Drive itself, in search of a dear little pair of patent-leather Gucci sandals I'd seen on a stylist at a fashion shoot.

I had often taken out-of-towners on a cursory crawl up one side of the street and down the other, a trip made in a gawking position as if we were slowing down on the freeway for a bloody traffic accident, but it had never occurred to me to actually park the car and go inside any of the shops. I always thought Beverly Hills a disappointingly garish affair, more dotty than stylish. It reminded me of Edward Lear's description of the Quangle Wangle:

> For his Hat was a hundred and two feet wide,
> With ribbons and bibbons on every side
> And bells, and buttons, and loops, and lace
> So that nobody ever could see the face
> Of the Quangle Wangle Quee.

But what did I know? At the time I was a cocky youngster who could get by with the sartorial equivalent of rubber bands and chewing gum and lots of élan. I learned this growing up in Portland, Oregon, where the young are very stylish in a punk/grunge/retro way. In New York, I probably would have shopped for grown-up shoes at Barney's, but when Angelenos do Barney's there's always something sophomorically austere about the effect, as if they just walked out of one of Woody Allen's "serious" movies. No, I wanted patent-leather Gucci sandals!

I parked in the public lot, right next to a Lincoln Mark VII,

my favorite car. I took this as auspicious. The Mark VII is a luxury
sedan masquerading as a muscle car, the kind of thing favored by
pimps and old ladies. You can't beat a Lincoln.

My first stop was the Prada store, in a side street just off Rodeo.
It's a tall, narrow space, with an upstairs loft, and the first impression is a small-scale echo of what it's like to walk into the Four
Seasons Hotel in New York, I. M. Pei's meditative hulk. Right
away the lobby of the Four Seasons makes you feel intimidated,
but it's an oddly pleasant sensation. The place is like a Japanese
teahouse on the scale of a gothic cathedral, if such can be imagined: a paper house made of marble and granite.

The Prada store was more like a gothic cathedral on the scale
of a Japanese teahouse, if you follow me. Here was a temple where
ethics and aesthetics met and blurred: here was austerity without
judgment, darkness without melancholy. Had the Germans and
the Japanese won World War II, the best high art of the resulting
dominant culture would have felt just like this.

Downstairs the dim, dun-colored walls receded in soft, shoji-
like shadows, the few, select handbags and shoes aglow like Orien-
tal vases, seeming to hover just above their shelves. All that was
missing was a branch of cherry blossoms. The well-lit staff of
lanky, hushed women gave me the briefest glance, both modest
and solicitous. Had it not been for the magic charm of the handbag on my shoulder, I might have run back into the street, but
instead I gave them the merest nod, and tiptoed past. Most of the
merchandise was kept away in blank-faced drawers, not to keep
customers' dirty paws and craving glances at bay, I imagined, but
so that each item might be separately revealed and ravished like a
pale, exquisite prisoner-whore. Upstairs, limpid sweaters pooled
on lacquered tables, and stiff iridescent shifts hung on sparse rods
like ceremonial vestments. Prada clothes are austere, ugly in the
way of Grace Kelly in *The Country Girl* or Isabella Rossellini in
certain moments from David Lynch films, an ugliness that is really
no more than beauty suddenly and unexpectedly denuded. Prada

(here it sounds like *prana*, the yogic, life-giving breath) is what one puts on immediately after this epiphanic mortification. The garment is clean, serene, humble, and brutal. The word "garment" always sounds odd to me, because it makes me think of the mean woolly suit of underclothes devout Mormons never remove even when bathing. To find this image sexy, you have to connect it up to the idea of Jean Genet on his knees, sucking on a policeman's .38 special, and then, somehow, it all works.

"I will never buy anything there," I said to myself as I walked out, as if this were an aspect of my mortality. I contemplated with great sadness the day when my handbag would finally succumb to the wear and tear of daily use, and I would no longer have a passport to enter the strange and dangerous region of design from which I'd just emerged.

Back on the street, I stumbled over a tiny Japanese girl in a Chanel T-shirt, staggering under a jangly Chanel backpack with huge, quilted logo, her whole ensemble screaming *"Duty free!"*

So I ducked into Chanel to cure my melancholy, and breathed in a different sensibility entirely, all whimsy and vanity fair, precious and perfumed. Chanel is *fun*—which is why it is so very, very difficult to wear. As a rule it is safe to say that before a woman is forty, a pair of earrings and a tube of lipstick are more than enough Chanel in her wardrobe unless she's seen all of Buñuel or read all of Borges. Never Truffaut or Proust—one doesn't want to be too French. Jerry Lewis and Jim Thompson are probationary options.

Once upon a time, I interviewed Joan Collins over lunch at Mr. Chow. The morning of the interview I stood in front of the mirror putting my Chanel earrings on and taking them off again. I was too young and inexperienced, I decided, to wear them in this situation. I decided to go bare-lobed, with just the lipstick and a spritz of Coco, and it was a lucky thing: when Joan arrived at the restaurant, she was wearing a navy blazer and a pair of Chanel earrings, and she looked magnificent. She had just won her two million dollars from Random House for the terrible book she'd had the balls to write, and she'd earned her Chanel, hands down. Even a belt would have been beyond reproach on her.

I doused myself in Cristalle at the black-and-glass counter, noticed that none of the salesclerks were over five feet tall—they looked like little cloisonné dolls—and returned to the street.

I paused in front of the Armani store's window display to offer up a prayer: "Do, Lord, spare us the depredations of Hollywood's infernal good taste!" Armani is fashion fail-safe, the uniform of the rude and famous, and I find the clothes equally lacking in character. Those ubiquitous putty-colored suits with the slumpy shoulders always look a size too big on whoever is wearing them, and always speak to me of an unpleasant admixture of caution and vanity, something of a McCarthy-era ambiance. It's perhaps my least favorite aesthetic—one that reeks of bad governments and dry-eyed sentimentality. These are weak-chinned power clothes for hypochondriacs, lobbyists, and closeted homosexuals. Well, I do have a pair of Armani jeans in my closet, and a little cocktail dress, but still.

I popped into Ferragamo to look at wallets, and when I emerged, I was briefly caught up in an eddy of young girls in boots and flowered minis and this season's sitcom haircut, all plump and youthful, too young, I imagine, to remember who Shannen Doherty was. "Oh, look!" they exclaimed. "There's the Franklin Mint Store!" tripping coltishly over one another in a rush for the window full of commemorative knickknacks. Watching them coo over the curios, I thought, *They're the ones who buy Joan Collins's novels, thus effectively passing the hat to pay for Joan's lovely Chanel earrings*, and I had a vision of Joan and me at Mr. Chow, the grande dame and her handmaiden feasting on the flesh of the Banal and the Ugly.

It was too much to bear, so, reminding myself that every socialist I've ever known has exhibited a keen appreciation for fine leather goods, I hurried on into the Gucci store, or more properly, the

Temple of Tom—Tom Ford being to Gucci what Oleg Cassini was to Jackie O.

To the left was a room full of luggage, the kind of luggage you would think Paul and Jane Bowles liked to carry to Ceylon and Morocco. Upstairs I handled the pinstriped suit I fell in love with in last month's *Vogue*, while a pair of chubby Asian-American girls tried on overcoats and called for the blond unisex salesclerks to send up some bubbly. Everyone smiled gaily at everyone else.

It was a strange experience, full of the girlish excitement of travel to a foreign country. I find Ford's work difficult to describe, because it is made of the kind of transparent culture that you live and breathe so much that you never fully perceive it. The typical Tom Ford suit, for example, provides what I'd have to call a medium of optimal subsistence as far as clothing goes—he's come as close as anyone to designing the Dymaxion Suit, the Dymaxion Blouse, the Dymaxion Shoe, the Dymaxion Purse. If Chanel is Buñuel, Gucci is J. G. Ballard: as fresh as an eroticized car crash in an alternate but highly moral universe.

In the shoe department, immediately I was taken in thrall by a pair of milk chocolate suede pumps, and it was all over. The moment I put them on my feet, I got an endorphin rush. I heard angels singing. I was Dorothy in Oz and Jeanne Moreau in *Diary of a Chambermaid*, all rolled into one. I did the math, and figured that if I wore them every day for two seasons, I could get the cost down to a dollar a day. Laughing at the mere thought of patent leather flip-flops, I wrote the check for the suede pumps in an endorphin haze and walked out into the gaudy L.A. sun a new woman.

As I waited across the street from the parking lot for the light to change, I stood next to a pair of podgy middle-aged men in ill-fitting pastel polo shirts and walking shorts, conversing in Arabic. I could tell by their tone and gestures that they were talking about me, though the only words of the discussion I understood were "high quality." They nudged each other back and forth, until one of them said, "You are movie star?" I smiled haughtily, pretended not to speak English, and walked on swinging my blond curls and my Prada handbag, leaving them in a cloud of Cristalle, feeling every inch the Arab tourist's wet dream and loving it.

It's so easy to scoff at the whorish gilt and gewgaws of Rodeo Drive, but I believe it's a seat of consciousness for the same reason that it's awful. When I was a college student and in Paris for the first time, I remember having an unsettling moment while touring the palace at Versailles. "My God," I thought to myself, "This place is *awful*. It's really *awful*." That anything so enormous and renowned could be that ugly came as a shock to my wee, puritan-provincial, teenage sense of style, and it impressed me: everything aesthetic was suddenly up for grabs. The only place I can compare Los Angeles to is Paris, which is the other place where people take huge risks in looking foolish, and once in a while pull off the kind of divine accident that is the only true origin of style.

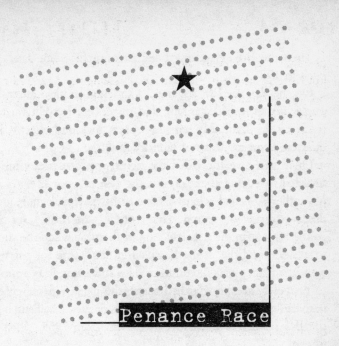

Penance Race

The IRS seized my bank account on a typical sunny afternoon. I first had inklings when my ATM card wouldn't work at my own bank, and a few days later I knew something was really amiss when I tried to write a check at Fred Segal for a pair of pants, and the check vetting service refused it. For some reason, I got a terrible cold right then, and went straight home, where I swilled Theraflu and hid without knowing why.

Over the years I had crept slowly up the scale from humble to comfortable: I obtained reliable and simultaneous access to roof, wheels, and food, and then moved considerably further upscale, meaning that, while I could not afford to buy things like health insurance and a car with air-conditioning, I no longer had to worry about spending the extra dollar for pre-peeled carrots in the supermarket, and I could spring for a really nice pair of shoes once a year.

Then the IRS seized my bank account for some taxes I owed back in 1985.

On the day the IRS got me, I happened to have no cash in my purse, not even a dollar bill, and my secured credit card was already to the limit. My working assets included exactly $4.50 in quarters from my stash of laundry money.

Once you owe the IRS back taxes, you can pretty much look forward to paying them off for the rest of your life. As I see it: My father is a mad scientist. One of his pet projects is to build a dome covering the moon. That's one of the short-term schemes. In the long term, he's worried about the time when the sun begins to weaken and die, so he has devised a scheme for carving it up well in advance of its expiration date and using it as a fuel source to propel Spaceship Earth through the galaxy in search of alternative energy sources. When and if this occurs, I will still be paying the IRS on that five grand I owe them from 1985, when I made fifteen.

In 1985, I was someone's secretary. I was just out of college and it was my first job, and I earned ten dollars per hour, which was a fortune. I bought a pair of pants at Bloomingdale's and was ecstatic. After a year, I bought my first computer, which was an Apple III, for $999, and wrote a six-hundred-page novel on it, which might have been terrible, but was less time-consumingly terrible than if I'd had to type the second draft on my Remington.

I've been poor before. Except for 1995, when I wrote a lot of articles about celebrity makeup and home decor, and the two years during which I was married to a middle-class Indian businessman, I've always been one or another kind of poor. There was student poor, which meant living on government loans and work-study and rooming with four people in a house with no heat and eating lots of instant ramen. Then there was bohemian poor, which meant living in a single-room-occupancy hotel in New York and sharing a bathroom with a bunch of schizophrenic winos. And there was single-mother poor, which meant putting twenty-five cents in the gas tank to get to the laundromat and back. But those were all deliberate forms of poverty. This was different; this was sudden, unrewarding, nonlifestyle poverty brought about by a simple turn of bad sociological weather.

Not that my plight was anything on the order of having one's house ripped up by a tornado, or getting hit by a bus when one has no health insurance. I feel the need to define poverty within the context of what I'm saying here. Nothing galls me like those people who say, "I'm soooo pooooor!" when what they mean is that they have a lot of credit card debt, or that they just blew all their ready cash on the down payment on a condo. Nancy, whom I love for richer or for poorer, etc., frequently borrows grocery money from me, which is fine, though when she says something about her poverty I occasionally point out that she has over ten grand in stocks and mutual funds, at which she gives me an impatient look and says, "Oh, but that doesn't count!" I always want to punch her in the face when she does this, whether I'm flush at the time or not. But then, my definition of poverty is probably just as obnoxious to someone who lives in a cardboard box.

That's the thing: poverty is insidiously relative. My neighbor's Mexican nanny and the nanny's husband—who's a janitor—just bought a house in the flats of Hollywood. Buying a house has probably been their diligently tended dream for a dozen years now. Were they poor before they bought their crappy little bungalow in a bad neighborhood? If so, are they still poor? I don't know, ultimately. All I can say is that I'm fiscally squalid and diseased, whereas they are pure and solvent as the driven snow, yet I probably make more per year than they do. I guess we're both poor, in some both larger and smaller sense of the word.

My working definition of poverty is this: (1) although I have a roof over my head, I'm chronically ten to fifteen days late with the rent and the landlord hates me; (2) I have a car, but it's unregistered and uninsured and may or may not run; (3) I have relatives who can't afford to lend me more than two hundred dollars per calendar year (although technically I could move in with them— in Oregon—in a crisis); and finally, (4) I have no assets I could conceivably liquidate. Oh, and (5) I have no credit. But then I never did have credit.

After the IRS seized my money, the first thing I did as a poor person was to borrow forty dollars and go to the supermarket, where in a foolish panic I bought all kinds of inedible staples: Bisquick mix, kidney beans, cabbage, a whole roasting chicken, pasta but no sauce. I went home and fussed over a hot stove for hours, making great pots of food meant to last for weeks. Of course, when you cook in a state of mental agitation, the food comes out tasting terrible, and I ended up with vats of swill on top of my stove: everything tasted like grease and mildew and too much Tabasco, and I threw it all out.

Thing is, poverty makes me hungry, always has. The first time I became actually, literally penniless, I was nineteen years old and hitchhiking around Europe. I eked out my dwindling supply of francs for days and days, and spent the last six of them, compellingly, on a big, greasy paper of *frites* with mayonnaise. I ate them with feral hunger, feeling consumed by food, not the other way around. Haven't you noticed how the poor eat fatty, comforting foods, while the rich tend to prefer mean, spiky, undercooked, architectonic meals?

The first time I threw a dinner party in L.A., I served pot roast with mashed potatoes, glazed carrots, and creamed spinach. Funny—I remember the menu, but not the guest list, though I think it was made up of Scott's Hollywood marginalia, writers, an agent, maybe an editor of mine thrown in. The appearance of a pot roast in their midst was greeted with such a dirty, voluptuous sense of shock, and everyone ate making swooning sounds and flashing back to childhoods spent in distant suburbs. But I was newly arrived in town and strapped for cash, and it never would have occurred to me to serve anyone Chilean sea bass with mango salsa and fat-free black bean timbales when we were eating at the Formica table in my Venice Beach kitchen. And it certainly wasn't what I wanted to eat now that I was stone broke.

For the next three days, I lay on the couch watching TV in the dark with the blinds closed, eating liverwurst sandwiches with lots of mayo and sweet pickles, and letting the messages pile up on the phone machine. I reacquainted myself with soap opera characters I hadn't seen since I had my wisdom teeth out at sixteen. I followed ladies' billiards on ESPN. Dramas and sitcoms seemed too good for me: at night I watched Dr. Gene Scott, the Home Shopping Network, and infomercials, my favorite of which was for something called the Infinite Dress. This was a polyester tube with two long straps that could be wrapped and tied to form unlimited fashion statements, all of which looked like things Cher wore in the seventies. If you sent in now, you got a free calendar showing thirty conjugated dresses for thirty days, and a matching scarf. I watched the Infinite Dress a lot, and I imagined what it would be like to have it, to have the Infinite Dress, the Infinite House, the Infinite Car. Perhaps I would write the Infinite Novel.

Meanwhile the phone kept ringing, my Infinitely broken phone with its horrible, continuous ring that just went on like an air-raid siren until either I answered or the machine picked up. I eyed it with hatred, wondering whether to take it into the bathroom and drown it or take it up to the roof and push it off, and then I had the inspired notion of actually taking it back to Circuit City for a refund. I'd bought the extended warranty—just like a dumb girl— and I still had a month to go on the plan. The phone sure as hell was broken or defective, and I sure could use the hundred and sixty bucks. So I packed it up and took off.

I have spent hours in line at the Department of Social Services. I've had tests run at the county hospital. I've even been detained for days by customs agents in New Delhi. But nothing can quite compare to the customer service department at Circuit City. When I got there, huddled masses were waiting in line clutching their cheap VCRs to their chests, while contemptuous clerks shuffled back and forth behind the white counter, looking for ballpoint

pens with ink in them while chatting on the phone with their
boyfriends. The woman in front of me sighed heavily every thirty
seconds, shifting the weight of her crappy, nonfunctioning tape
deck from one formidable haunch to another. When her turn
came, she slammed it on the counter and began a jaunty, heckling
tirade that the bored clerk only watched with one Nefertiti-lined
eye, while arguing on the phone with her boyfriend.

When my turn came, the clerk looked at my nasty box of phone
with a lazy eye, then poked at a keyboard for a few moments,
shaking her head. She pushed the phone and my receipt back
across the counter at me. "Come back in three days," she said,
turning to another clerk and beginning a blow-by-blow recounting
of the boyfriend conversation.

"Why?" I asked.

She told me my receipt was too old and I wasn't in the computer.

"Why three days?" I asked. "What will have changed?"

At this, she took the receipt back and looked at it again, long
and hard, as if it were a prisoner she were deciding whether or
not to grant parole. The phone rang, and she answered it, and
then she helped the person on the phone with whatever they
needed helping with, and then five minutes later, she came back
and looked at me warily, as if I were some stray postal worker
who might shoot her. "Well?" I said, nodding to my receipt, which
she still held in her hand, though she no longer knew it. She
looked at it again, long and hard, then picked up her phone, dialed
a number, and spoke to someone on the other end for a long time,
poking at the computer with a pencil eraser from time to time.
She hung up and asked to see the phone, which I had assiduously
boxed up. She unpacked it, and examined every inch of it, slowly
and aimlessly, then she said, "Leave it here and come back in seven
days." I asked to see the manager. The clerk left again. When she
came back, she shoved my phone down the counter and shouted
"Next!"

The black woman who had been in line behind me stepped up

to the counter and set down her VCR. She looked at me. "That's a shitty phone," she said. "I had one of those."

The manager, who was ominously white, came and looked down his long, warty nose at me with something beyond hatred, that evil undead "You're an insect I squash you" look one associates with mid-level civil servants and probation officers. I was the only other white person there, so he felt obliged to treat me as if I were some kind of race traitor. White people, his look told me, are supposed to throw broken phones away. "Why did you wait so long to bring it back?" he said, in a tone that indicated I was somewhere on the moral level of a woman who smokes while she's pregnant. I knew I was wasting my time.

When I got to the car, the door handle broke off in my hand. I climbed in from the passenger side, thinking that I would probably be doing so for a long time, and making a mental note to avoid wearing dresses for the duration of my poverty. It struck me that I was now, in fact, *crawling*.

Seven days later, I went back to Circuit City, and was told that my phone was broken, but I couldn't get cash, just a store credit, because it had been "too long."

This time, the car died completely on the way home, which is why, several days later when I had to interview a minor celebrity at a restaurant in Beverly Hills, I ended up having my first experience with L.A. public transportation.

The trip to Beverly Hills took four hours, and I rode a total of three buses. At one point I got off to transfer and found myself standing at a bus stop on a traffic island situated at the confluence of several rushing streams of automobiles. There was no way on or off the island, except by bus, and for a long time, I stood there alone, in my nice Beverly Hills–restaurant clothes, growing sootier and sweatier and making a mental list of the three things I would have brought with me had I known I was to be stranded on a desert island. Eventually, a bus dropped off a couple of man Fridays and two Latino guys who looked dressed to valet-park; a while after that, my transfer bus arrived, and I was rescued. I was the only white person on my entire journey who wasn't drunk or on Thorazine.

I conducted my interview, though the minor celebrity was a little shocked when I sat down and ordered a huge plate of fish and chips and wolfed them down with beer. But I didn't care.

My provisional salvation came a month after my fall, when some magazine finally sent me a check big enough to pay my rent and get the car fixed. I had no access to banking facilities, with the IRS lien still hanging over me like the sword of Damocles, so I had to take it to one of those "We cash any check! No ID!" places. The clerk behind the bulletproof glass was friendly enough as he took my picture and fingerprinted me and called the magazine and the bank that issued the check. At the window next to me a white man in filthy chinos, a raincoat, and a ratty fedora was holding up all kinds of dirty, crumpled envelopes and receipts and shouting, "Everything was stolen! Everything! I'm a secret agent with the FBI!"

I leaned up to the window, real close, and gave the clerk a maniacal leer. I whispered, "The IRS is out to get me! That's why I can't go to the bank, they'll seize everything!"

He gave me my money anyway.

The worst over, I still keep wondering what I had done wrong. Not that I got hooked up with a lame accountant, certainly, or that I failed to invest wisely or start a nest egg or a mutual fund or an IRA. I mean what I did that was *wrong*. You see, I finally realized that poverty is a sin. Wealth in L.A. is something that comes upon you once you've achieved the proper state of ecstatic transport. This is something hard work or education can't get you. The wealthy are divinely inspired, like Pentecostals who've been touched by the hand of God and fall down speaking in tongues. Clearly, impecuniousness is the mark of the devil, and my fall from grace must mean that in some fundamental way, I am an unfit Angeleno.

I am especially unfit now, because during my poverty I gained a good ten pounds. This is a radical thing in Los Angeles, where through all my tribulations I've learned to appreciate one maxim: as cleanliness is to godliness, thinness is to wealth. That is, thinness is the L.A. version of the Protestant work ethic, the focal point of the city's rather austere notion of hedonism—for only in L.A. is hedonism conceived of as a discipline. Being vain about one's body is something one works at and sacrifices for. The perfect L.A. body is as weird as some bizarre breed of show dog. It isn't really something you can achieve short of surgery and a six-hour-a-day workout, but achieving it isn't really the point; striving for it is.

Absolutely everyone who counts is too rich and too thin, and just to be part of the game, one is duty bound to feel five pounds overweight at all times; it's a kind of penance race.

Being fat is probably even worse than being poor, and when I was poor, I grew fat, fat, fat! I outgrew all my trousers, and had to hit the Salvation Army's half-off-all-clothing sale in Glendale, where I stocked up on used Levi's and cords and baggy gangsta pants. I took them home and put them on—and then something weird happened.

All of a sudden, I looked great again. I noticed it in the mirror right away. I thought it might be part of a temporary, bacon burger–induced reverse body dysmorphia, that instead of thinking I looked too fat when I was in fact too thin, I was deluding myself by thinking myself foxy when I was in fact a cow. But then, one day in the supermarket, when I was spending a long, long time trying to read the unit pricing on the dairy shelf, an exceedingly young, good-looking Latino boy came up and asked for my phone number. I immediately murmured a discouraging blandishment without thinking, and only blushed when he walked away. He disappeared down an aisle, then came back and said, "Are you sure? Do you have a boyfriend?" I said yes, stupidly, and he walked away again, then came back a third time and said, "He's a lucky guy." I was left in a deep state of shock.

Nancy came over to use the pool, and I tried to explain my lack of dismay at my weight, to her growing puzzlement. "You're so funny," she said. "If anything, *maybe* you've gained four pounds."

(She was being polite, not saying the dreadful "five.") We argued for a while, but Nancy refused to grant that I was fat, even though I said I liked it and wanted to be fat. She equally refused to grant that she was thin. She often remarks on how much men like her to be fatter than she is. But then Nancy, who runs marathons and has invisible mutual funds, will always think she's five pounds too heavy, even if she falls in love with Croesus and marries him, or sells a screenplay to Disney for a million bucks, or writes a classic novel.

Is the mutual fund the fatty deposit on the thigh?

Maybe, I think. Maybe it's better to be poor.

Maybe it's not so bad to be crawling through your Volkswagen to get to the driver's seat, maybe there's an idea of leanness that's available to me because I have no safety net and apparently no compunctions, and I wonder, when we build the dome around the moon, or cut up the sun, what kind of wealth or poverty will be there, and will there be a Circuit City on Mars? In a Dymaxion Constellation, is anyone fat or thin or rich?

☆

Pretty soon I noticed that in fact my big, proud ass was drawing attention everywhere I went, and I enjoyed no end of meaningful eye contact with strange men, none of whom had car phones. These were robust, easygoing, manly Angelenos, many of them nonwhite. Guys who had real jobs and ate burgers and probably liked unironic sex. It seems silly to say, but the discovery of these ubiquitous guys, and their discovery of me, I count as an unlooked-for, last-minute salvation.

One late summer night, bills kind of paid, I wove through the tables on the patio at Caffe Luna, on my way to meet Janine for dinner and a brief financial consult with Andrei. I was wearing clothes that did nothing to disguise my replenished hips and first-time-ever fulsome tits, and I was getting the looks there, too, even though I was the only girl in the place who didn't look like a boy.

I felt like I had back when I was the first girl in my school to get a punk haircut.

Janine watched me as I approached the table and said, "You look fantastic, girl, have you lost weight?"

Me? No; I'm as rich and as thin as the day I was born.

Psycho-
Physiological
Investigations

The slide on the screen is a grainy black-and-white picture of a Volkswagen bug. A naked man crouches on his haunches next to the rear fender, as if he were changing a tire.

"This is the love bug," Stuart Swezey says in a dry, collegiate voice. Stuart is the owner of the Amok Bookstore and editor of *The Amok Journal, Sensurround Edition: A Compendium of Psychophysiological Investigations,* which is the subject of his lecture. "In 1973, an article called 'The Love Bug' was published in the *Journal of Forensic Sciences,* and I'd like to read a little of it to you:

> Reconstruction of the events leading to the subject's death indicated that after removing his clothing and donning the chain harness, he attached himself to the back bumper of the Volkswagen by the ten-foot length of chain. Then, with the car in low gear and the steering wheel in a fixed ten

o'clock right position, the car slowly ran in concentric circles. It is not known whether the subject simply jogged after the moving automobile, or allowed himself to be dragged. . . . When the subject tired of this form of exercise, he apparently approached the car with the intent of taking it out of gear and turning off the ignition. At this point there was a serious "pilot error" when he neglected to detach himself from the chain on the bumper of the Volkswagen before he approached the car. As he approached the car the chain attached to the bumper became slack, and the back wheel of the car rolled over the chain. The chain began then to revolve onto the back axle. The subject must have realized his plight almost immediately and possibly sustained many abrasions fighting for his life against the ever-shortening chain. Subsequently, however, the chain wound completely around the axle, and the subject was asphyxiated against the rear fender of the Volkswagen . . .

"So that brings us to the subject of autoerotic fatalities and autoerotic asphyxia. The powerful psychophysiological matrix is created by the combination of secrecy, the risk of death, personally choreographed rituals, erotic excitement, and the rush of hypoxia."

☆

The thing I like best about my new neighborhood is that I live within walking distance of Amok. The store is a tall, narrow, shotgun space with a relatively sparse assortment of books displayed along one wall, not the kind of place you go for cookbooks or guidebooks, though they do stock the *Anarchist's Cookbook* and a guide to famous crime scenes in Hollywood. This is where you could get Jim Thompson novels before he was Jim Thompson, and books by Nikola Tesla, and John Waters, and William Burroughs, and the Marxist anthropologist Marvin Harris. There are true-crime paperbacks and Tom of Finland gay porn comics and

surrealist collage-novels by Max Ernst. And how nice to walk into
a bookstore where instead of categories like "Women's Studies"
and "Gay Studies" and "African-American Lit." the engraved
brass markers on the shelves say things like "Mayhem," "Exotica,"
and "Neuropolitics."

The store sits on a popular stretch of Vermont Avenue above
Hollywood Boulevard, in Los Feliz Village, which was once part
of L.A.'s Little Italy but has now been taken over mostly by elderly
Armenians with blue-and-pink hair, and younger people with blue-
and-pink hair of a more intense hue. On Vermont Avenue, old-
fashioned Italian bakeries and gray, forbidding gift shops so old
they look as if you might find the Ark of the Covenant gathering
dust in the basement are interspersed with piercing salons and
clothing stores that sell holographic vinyl miniskirts. Right next
door to Amok is the Dresden Room, where an ancient couple
named Marty and Elayne have been doing a lounge act at the
piano bar for decades, serenading the spiders in the corkboard
walls, until the hipster crowds descended and made the place so
popular on Saturday nights that it now it reads as fake Disneyland
retro, even though it's not.

Stuart is the unofficial curator of L.A.'s fringe culture; when the
BBC needs to interview someone for a documentary on tiki lounge
art, they come to him. But while the other shopkeepers on Vermont Avenue are likely to be dyed and tattooed, with shirts but-
toned the wrong way on purpose, Stuart is assiduously neat and
well-groomed, with a Tom Sawyer niceness about his outward demeanor—and more than a little Twain-y harshness within. Stuart
is what I always think of as the prototypical native Angeleno, in
that he's at once broadly sane and deeply weird. I take this to be
an evolutionary adaptation to the environment, a brave new nor-
malcy none but the few who grew up in L.A.—and survived—can
even begin to know.

Since I became an official regular at Amok, Stuart asked me if
I'd like to help write blurbs and reviews for the new *Amok Dis-
patch*. Every few years, Stuart puts out a massive mail-order cata-

logue, a "sourcebook of the extremes of information in print," according to the subtitle. As Stuart explained the deal, I could go upstairs and root around among the review copies, and anything I took home and wrote up, I could keep. This was the bibliophile's offer of a lifetime, so I said yes, and walked out with a conspiracy-theory biography of John Dillinger, an instruction manual for armed robbery, something called *Dirty Tricks Cops Use,* and a book that featured glossy photographs of Peter the Great's collection of human teeth and pickled infants. I would no longer be needing Barnes & Noble, I could see already.

So of course I devoured *The Amok Journal,* an anthology of materials Stuart described as "an imaginary research report from an institute that would be investigating psychophysiological phenomena," and when he gave a slide show to promote it, I went and sat in a room with a hundred or so artists, writers, dominatrixes, and other people dressed in black.

☆

The next slide, after the Love Bug, is a picture of a man in his hospital bed. "This is Bob Flanagan," Stuart says. "Bob suffered from cystic fibrosis. This is from an installation piece called *Visiting Hours,* where Bob was in the Santa Monica Museum, installed in a hospital room, with many of his artworks around him. The significance lies in the way that he eroticized medical imagery and paraphernalia, and he actually used autoerotic practices both in his work and in his life. Now I'd like to show you a video clip from a show Bob did at Amok, called 'Nailed.'"

In the taped performance, Flanagan, who styles himself "Supermasochist," nails his scrotum to a board and hangs by his wrists from a scaffold. It's a strangely moving performance, if you know that this artwork is coming out of lifelong illness, that it's part of a dialogue with pain and suffering. A long time ago, when I lived in New York, a friend in L.A. told me over the phone that they'd just seen some "performance art" by a masochist with cystic fibrosis, who I realize now was Flanagan. I rolled my eyes at the time, laughed, and said something like "Jesus Christ, what next? Being in L.A. has made you soft in the head." To which I got a vague reply like "Well, I guess you had to be there." Now that I am there, so to speak, it looks less frivolous. For a moment I step outside myself and wonder if I'm just so desensitized that it takes something like the sight of genital mutilation to move me, but I don't think that's it at all: lots of artists express pain in their art, but this is the first time I've ever seen pain used as a medium for the expression of something deeper, more on the order of mastery of the soul under crisis. It is, I must admit, something real, with the backbone of poetry. I think of something Stuart said earlier, quoting André Breton: "Beauty will be compulsive, or will not be at all."

"The last psychophysiological investigation I'm going to get to today is trepanation," Stuart says, "and that's drilling a hole in your skull. This I regard as a very direct approach to the mind-body split." He gets a laugh. The slide is a picture of a woman, smiling eagerly. Her head is bandaged, and she's drilling a hole in the center of her head. Her expression is that of a housewife in a 1950s ad for a work-saving kitchen appliance. "Trepanation goes back thousands of years, to ancient practices in Peru and Tibet," Stuart says. "This woman runs for Parliament today on a trepanation platform."

The lecture is over. We've seen lots of other slides and video clips this evening, of cargo cults in New Guinea, of William Burroughs and Brion Gysin, Bataille, Breton, and Dali, J. G. Ballard, and Balinese trance ceremonies, as well as video from Jacopetti's *Mondo Cane*—unpleasantly hilarious footage of a turtle dying on the beach of radioactive Bikini Island.

In his deadpan voiceover, Stuart sums up: "In conclusion, I would like to say that these examples of convulsive beauty and transcendent experience have come about by people using themselves as guinea pigs and trying out the various things . . . so I hope that you can do the same yourself!"

He gets a laugh, and great applause. I can tell when I stand up that there are endorphins in my bloodstream, though I don't yet know what part of the evening I'm high on. It's all been grotesque and comic, a dark mirror of a TV talk show, but different, the opposite of the kind of therapeutic voyeurism that would have us all joining "codependency" and "repressed memory syndrome" support groups just to mooch off each other's neuroses. The only therapy available here would have us dying in shame, alone, of some absurd, misunderstood desire. That notion of the ignominious death suddenly strikes me as heroic, and I know what I'm high on: nothing less than the ancient ethic of rugged individualism!

After the lecture, a bunch of us go out to a corny Mexican restaurant for margaritas and nachos, Stuart and his girlfriend, me, Anne, Anne's ex-husband, some other people I don't know. I sit next to some person's garrulous husband, a salesman who is high up in the Toastmasters organization, so I hear all about this strange middle American club of businesspeople who meet in the banquet rooms of Holiday Inns and give speeches on things like human resources management. It strikes me as by far the weirdest thing I've heard this evening, and I know I'm never going back to whatever part of the earth I came from; I'm like a little flippered creature that took a walk outside the warm comforting waters of the primordial sea and suddenly found it had lost its gills.

Guns & Ammo

The car is my bane. My '71 Volkswagen squareback jerks and lurches like a rickety old roller coaster. Anyone who rides with me grips the sides of their seat unconsciously. If I'm feeling at all fragile, the car can finish me. I view my daily encounter with it as a planned and scheduled physical assault. The fact is, no car trip can be survived undamaged, and the basic substrate of my daily existence is this war of attrition against the nerves.

And it's not just the deep-seated, conceptual horror of hopping from island to island in a torrential sea wherein *hundreds of thousands of total strangers* zip around at high speed, encased in tons of metal. In the summer months, the Volkswagen is an immolation chamber, the windshield like a magnifying glass under the sun. Within minutes of climbing in I'm overheated to the point of derangement, nasty, sweaty, cursing, often in tears, wet and half-blind furious. By the time I get anywhere, the car has utterly destroyed me.

It's a dry, brittle, sudden rage. Late August, in the car—always in the car, these accesses of the primitive, something I achieved only once or twice a year, maybe, when I lived in cold, car-free climates, but which I now experience almost every day: I almost don't see the line of cars stopped in front of me, half a block back from the light, in heavy mid-morning traffic somewhere near Park LaBrea. I skid to a stop, but barely. I've had a bad day already, and I'm late. My sense of forward-moving necessity winds tighter and tighter as the light ahead goes green, then red, then green again, and I come to a boil. I let out a long scream and beat my fists on the dash. I try to tear the steering wheel out by its roots like a bad tooth. I beat up my car, from the inside, punching and kicking. I'm not so much crying as foaming all over, apopleptic with hate.

One day I walked over to Amok and dropped in on Stuart. "Stuart, do you still have that book about gunshot wounds?" I asked.

"You doing research?" Stuart asked. He hunted through the shelves and found the book I wanted, which was a criminology textbook called *Gunshot Wounds: Practical Aspects of Firearms, Ballistics, and Forensic Techniques*, by Vincent J. M. Di Maio. It was, I noted with a twinge, priced at eighty-five dollars.

"No," I said. "I want to shoot somebody. I want to pick out the kind of wound I'd like to inflict, so I'll know which gun to buy."

I weighed the book in my hand, dark red with white lettering, 331 pages. The price gave it a koranic heft, like something that held great truth and wisdom, secrets. At eighty-five dollars there was nothing camp or vulgar about the purchase.

I sighed, and Stuart gave me a ten percent discount and rang up the book. As is often the case, a couple of Stuart's friends were hanging around near the register. "I have my dad's old thirty-eight special," said a girl named Sarah who looked like a grad student. "I'd recommend a revolver. You don't have to clean them as often, and they never jam."

"You know, they have these little forty-five automatics you can get for fifty, sixty bucks," said one guy.

"Thanks," I said to both of them, "I'll remember that."

Unlike other people who get involved with handguns, I did not have any illusions about using the weapon to defend myself against surly strangers. Once, in New York, I was assaulted in an elevator by a big, burly drunk who looked like Bluto on *Popeye*, and who made big, threatening, slobbery noises as he advanced on me. I managed to slip out of the elevator, but instead of running away I picked up an empty bottle off the floor and tried to hit him in the head with it. I think it was an Olde English 800 bottle, probably recently discarded by Bluto himself. The bottle only bounced, making a silly *gong!* sound, and he socked me in the eye, sending me flying into the wall. It was all very cartoonish. I did get away after that, since he was really too out of it to be anything but very large, but I learned that self-defense can in some cases be construed as mere vanity. Aw, I wanted to break a bottle over a bad guy's head! Shooting him would have been just as silly, and maybe I would have shot him if I'd had a gun, and for the very same reason—just to try it.

My real reasons for wanting to be armed and dangerous were somewhat different.

The idea truly began to form during a conversation I had with a male friend one day as we were driving in my car past a billboard that showed a male/female couple in boxing gloves and Everlast trunks gazing hungrily at each other over raised fists and the caption "Call 1-800-4 BOXING" Since he spent two or three hours at the gym every day, he wasn't about to let singles boxing pass by without comment.

"I don't understand this whole thing about women learning to box," he said. "The point is, no matter how good they get, they'd never be able to take me out."

"That's not it at all," I said, ignoring the obvious advantages I could see in being able to pulverise even small men and other women. "If I wanted to take you out, all I'd have to do is run you over with my car."

Later I took to brooding in earnest on the subject of deadly force and absolute, versus relative, power. I wondered whether even a situation such as the drunk guy in the elevator would have turned out differently if I'd been a person who knew how to kill people, and knew that I knew it, at all times. Maybe I would have swung the bottle a lot harder, for instance. Or maybe I would have pulled a .22 out of my purse and shot him in the foot, just to make an emphatic point. Why shouldn't all idiots be shot in the foot?

I was suddenly very tired of being an overeducated girl who could do no more harm than write a really mean poem. I didn't want to turn into a neurotic bitch. I didn't want to take up boxing. I didn't want to slash anyone's tires or call them repeatedly and hang up, or take over a large corporation and fire everybody, or get really, really fat or really, really thin.

There's no polite way to say this, but it became important to me to know how to kill. I thought that if people knew I knew how to kill them, and knew that I knew that I knew, they would treat me a lot better, by and large. It was that simple. And if I knew that they knew that I could kill them, should I so choose, I thought that I might be able to experience a sense of invulnerable calm.

Given my antipathy toward all things automotive, I decided that the '71 Volkswagen was not to be my weapon of choice. In truth, I did not feel sufficiently in control of the car or the car's environment; I was its driver, but not its master. With a car attack, chances were good the victim would survive in a semi-vegetable state and linger on for years, painting miniature landscapes with his teeth or creating unified theories of everything. The idea of inadvertently unleashing such a creature gave me the creeps. I wanted more control than that. If I was going to maim, I thought it far preferable to wreck a kneecap, for example, inflicting a permanent injury that would be annoying but not inspiring.

So, knowing exactly what I wanted, I cracked the book's luxurious spine that night and read it cover to cover. Later, when I knew more about guns, I had to read it again. I learned, for instance, that bullets do not drill through the flesh in a straight line. Rather, the kinetic energy let off by the bullet "flings" the surrounding tissue away from the bullet's path, so that the speeding bullet creates a balloonlike "temporary cavity" as it passes through, which later collapses to form the "permanent wound track." Different kinds of tissue react differently, too. Liver tissue, for example, is particularly nonresilient. A shot through the liver will leave a wound almost as big as the temporary cavity. Lung tissue, on the other hand, is extremely elastic and has a very low density, and a shot through the lung will produce relatively little tissue destruction. This all seemed like the kind of stuff you'd want to know before you started shooting people.

The book was heavily illustrated. I'm squeamish when it comes to gore. From the morgue photographs accompanying the text, I decided that, for instance, I never wanted to shoot anyone in the head with a .357 magnum at a one-foot range. I also decided that if I ever wanted to kill myself, I'd take some kind of pill, thank you, rather than run the risk of living for 1 hour and 34 minutes with a head shaped like an anvil, like the poor slob on page 211. Gunshot wounds, I was beginning to realize, are not as glamorous as one thinks; instead of a neat little abstract hole through which life may drain out elegantly, the damage is likely to be a grotesque and almost incidentally fatal deformity of the human outline. The possibilities were becoming much more graphic, and at the same time more powerfully abstract.

At one point the author advised that a corpse should always be X-rayed with its clothes on: "In one case the bullet exited the right chest and fell into the inside pocket of a jacket. A hole was present in the bottom of the pocket, and the bullet then fell into the lining. It would not have been found had X ray not shown it to be in the clothing." This image struck home, as I thought of all the times I'd been unable to find what had damaged me, probably because I'd been too hasty to strip myself bare in looking for it.

The most compelling illustrations were the ballistics tests, in which bullets of varying caliber were shot into clear gelatin blocks supposed to simulate the density and elasticity of flesh. People are always saying guns and cigarettes are phallic. I've always been skeptical about that, because it seemed too obvious to be true. But the wound paths in the gelatin blocks looked distinctly vaginal. You wouldn't know this by looking at an entrance wound or an exit wound, but if you ever saw a gelatin block showing the wound path, it would look like one of those cross-sectional posters in a Planned Parenthood office: everything important is below the surface. This image, unlike the guns and the cigarettes, is hidden enough to be breathtaking when it reveals itself. Looking at the bullet paths, I felt like Georgia O'Keeffe looking into a flower for the first time. It queered my vengeful, self-righteous pursuit of power by any means necessary, tweaking it over into something new: gun lust.

Now when I thought of holding a gun in my hand, the blood rushed to my fingers. My gestures changed, even thinking about the metal in my hand, its weight. For weeks, I stopped in every pawnshop and gun store I saw, just so I could hold guns and also watch them be handled: I loved to watch the paunchy, middle-aged gun salesmen turn themselves into erotic dynamos just by pulling back the slide on an automatic. It's the way the body acts with a gun. Street kids don't have it, they don't have the body language, but real gun handlers move with gentleness and authority, casual and quick and minimal and very, very calm.

The movies sometimes come close to approximating this weapons sexiness, but usually they miss by making it more and not less. What's devastating is the incredible stillness that is possible when a man or a woman is holding a gun. It's what gives cops their allure. I always thought it was a kinky thing on my part, a wallowing urge, that attraction to cops, but it turns out every girl I know has a thing for them, and now I know why: it's that vicious, gentle stillness of the armed.

When I went to the corner liquor store for a bottle of Gatorade, I picked up copies of *Guns & Ammo, Handguns, Handgunning,* and *Combat Handguns.*

"Are you a hit man?" the checkout clerk asked.

I read for hours, learning all about stopping power and the Weaver stance.

I went downtown to the L.A. Gun Club, where I was the only non-Asian customer, and they tried to sell me a Glock 26, which was "popular with the ladies." I didn't want a Glock. I shot a Beretta and a SigSauer on the range, both .380s, and decided I didn't like either one. I didn't like the hordes of Japanese tourists on all sides of me, either—little girls in pastel pants, holding .45s with both hands and giggling. The place was expensive, too, and I never went back.

I went to the taxidermy shop on Hollywood Boulevard, which also sells guns, and looked at a couple of old European .22 revolvers, cute little things I could have kept in my Prada bag. I liked one of them, but it was five hundred dollars, and it didn't seem right, buying a five-hundred-dollar gun on Hollywood Boulevard. I could see buying the hot pink .45 with the plastic pearl handle, if I were going to run out right then and shoot my pimp or my agent dead on the glitter-flecked pavement in front of Mann's Chinese.

At a pawnshop in Beverly Hills, I asked the Armenian girl to show me the guns; she gave me a look and went to get her father. He gave me a look, too, and said, "It's illegal to carry a gun, you know."

He said it as if I'd just mentioned I was planning to commit welfare fraud. Like I was one of "those evil, stupid people."

"Yes, I know that," I said. "You do sell guns, don't you?"

Finally, he asked for my driver's license, then opened the display case, but all he had were silly, engraved commemorative-edition revolvers that reminded me of those gun- or boot- or ship-shaped liquor bottles my best friend's dad kept in the den when I was a kid. I decided that an even worse sale point for firearms than a taxidermy shop on Hollywood Boulevard would be an Armenian pawnshop in Beverly Hills.

I went back to Amok and got a couple more books, *How to Kill* and *Kill Without Joy!* I learned a lot reading these, including how to kill somebody with a tennis ball, or a bag of dry ice, or a can of chewing tobacco, or an ordinary newspaper, as well as proper garrotting technique. This was all very amusing in a James Bond way, but I also picked up wisdom on handgunning that was more to my taste than the "Wowee! This baby's got stopping power!" vein of advice running through the gun magazines. The extra research proved my instincts right: I was meant to be a nasty crack shot with a quiet little gun, not a bull with a cannon.

By the time I got to King's Gun Works, in the Valley, I knew what I wanted. A guy with a beard showed me the Colt and the Ruger, both .22 target pistols. I hefted them both, first the Ruger, then the Colt. I liked the Colt better. It felt good in my hand, like a second center of gravity. It didn't look the way I imagined my gun would look—it was high-tech and sharp, not rugged and dull.

I went home to study for my firearms safety test; a week later I went back.

Another guy with a beard showed me the guns again. He advised the Ruger, but the Colt fit my hand better and I took it. Another customer, also a guy with a beard, looked on approvingly. "Yeah, I like that Colt, that's a nice gun. I always say, every woman in this country should be given a concealed-carry permit. That would level the playing field."

I thought it a chivalrous remark, for a complete stranger.

I went back to King's several times in the process of buying my gun, and got to know the guys. They put me on to a good range in Burbank, where I've been shooting ever since.

When I'm shooting, my head is empty of all else. The precision of gesture, the power, the noise, the hairline focus of attention: it's the only thing I ever do, the only thing I've ever done, that is entirely of a piece. I started out wanting to kill people, and now shooting is pure abstraction, a meditation. Part of the meditation, of course, and the reason it works for me when no kind of yoga or TM or other doe-eyed sport ever did, is that it's part and parcel of death and rage and desire and pain.

Me, I long to be the exact opposite of a bodhisattva, something more like a cowboy, or a tough-guy novelist, or a mad scientist. It isn't peace that makes existence bearable, but a sense of being up against it, of pushing back. The only comfort zone in this life lies on the extreme edge of possibility and decision, the place where it all comes to rest on the trigger.

Escape
from
L.A.

⭐ I am not a big fan of the movies. I probably see five or six a year, outside of those I've had to suffer professionally. So far this year, I've seen *Twister, Dead Man,* and *Independence Day* for pleasure, and *Primal Fear* and *Mr. Holland's Opus* for pain. I like a good action movie above all, as action seems to me to be the one and only thing movies do so much better than books. I could watch national monuments blow up all day long: earthquakes, tidal waves, alien invasions, World War III. My favorite movies have no sex and lots of violence.

The other thing I'm fond of in movies is the notion of dystopia. I love *Mad Max, Blade Runner,* and *Brazil.* I liked *Carnosaur* so much more than *Jurassic Park* despite the corny effects, because of mad scientist Diane Ladd's perverted notion that dinosaurs were "better" than humans and deserved to rule the earth—a perfect dystopian worldview, so much more compelling than Spielberg's squidgy goodie-baddie notion of order in a cold universe as a deus ex Hallmark. And then there's my favorite movie, *The President's Analyst,* with James Coburn joining forces with the CIA, some acid-dropping hippies, and Russian spies to do battle against the evil forces of the Phone Company. Now, there's what I call a cinematic vision!

So of course I dragged my friend Rob off to see *Escape from L.A.* right when it came out, even though everyone was telling me how bad it was. Rob grew up in Bakersfield, so he shares my interest in dystopian worlds. We both thought it fitting to go see this movie at Universal City, which is a kind of inescapable dystopia all its own. A friend of mine who lives in New Delhi wrote me recently that talks are under way to build a Citywalk on the subcontinent, which is an even worse idea than EuroDisney, if you ask me, and almost as bad as Celebration, Florida, the planned community Disney is building in the shadow of Disney World and Epcot Center. But then, a main characteristic of any dystopia is that it arises from human folly, a Town-of-Frankenstein dream gone haywire.

We got there early, and strolled through Citywalk, which is a little like being two inches tall and lost inside a pinball machine. Everything glows, rings, whistles, or bounces, and I think the architectural style is deconstructivist, so the whole thing looks like something you need special glasses to see.

"Hey, I never noticed that," Rob said, pointing out a neon sign overhead, a fifties blonde with a neon caption that read, like a drunken non sequitur: "Through these gates pass the most beautiful girls in the world."

We looked at each other and shrugged. "And a lot of Japanese people," I said. The whole place was geared toward Japanese predilections: a baseball memorabilia store, a sci-fi store full of Godzilla toys. I imagined that in the rain, Citiwalk would look just like *Blade Runner,* only cute.

"It's pornographic," Rob said.

"Everything's pornographic," I said. "I took Tyrone to the video store yesterday, and he accidentally got loose in the porno section. He picked up a porno Batman movie, and we had quite a showdown over it."

We retreated to the bookstore/coffee shop to browse. Actually, at first we didn't know it was a bookstore, there was so much potpourri-scented frippery all over the place, clinging to the walls and the shelves, as if someone had set off a Laura Ashley splatter bomb at ground zero. What books there were seemed to be about herb gardening, feng shui, wedding plans, and mysteries by and for women who love cats. Tucked in the back was a "literature" section, where I overheard a conversation between two teenage girls, one blond, one Latina, both in long hair and lip gloss, penciled brows and baggy flannel shirts.

"I'm kinda into Faust these days," said the brunette girl, popping her gum.

"Yeah," said the blonde. "But which version? I think Goethe's is more interesting than Marlowe's."

"Oooh!" the brunette squealed. "I gotta have this James Joyce."

"He wrote the *Something-berries*—no, it was the *Dubliners*"— she pronounced it *Doobliners,* as in *Scooby Doo*—"Gawd, of course, duh."

They moved down the aisle, away from the Great Works section.

"I'm disappointed in the Thoreau collection."

"What's that?"

The blonde picked up an oversized volume from a shelf. "*The Great American Bathroom Book*."

I found Rob again near the calendars, all of which featured cats, angels, or pigs. "I just ran into two intelligent life forms from outer space posing as teenagers," I said.

"Good," said Rob, "the movie's about to start. Let's go."

"What I really want to know," I said, "is what the first generation of teenagers to come of age in Celebration, Florida, is going to be like."

We watched the movie.

Escape from L.A. has Kurt Russell reprising the role of Snake

from the earlier, wonderful *Escape from New York*. In the sequel,
an earthquake has divided L.A. from the rest of the country, and
by the year 2013 it's being used as a Devil's Island, where people
are shipped off for such crimes as using foul language, eating red
meat, and listening to heavy metal. The moral of the story is "Mo-
rality is evil." I'm not kidding. Though on a deeper level the movie
also asks the eternal question "Whatever happened to Adrienne
Barbeau?" Well, the movie did contain several absolutely juicy
moments: Kurt Russell and Peter Fonda surfing a tidal wave; Kurt
Russell about to be parted out by cosmetic-surgery vampires; Kurt
Russell racing the shot clock in a baseketball arena while the firing
squad waits; Mann's Chinese overrun by knife-wielding punks and
strippers; the final shoot-out in Disneyland; and of course, Steve
Buscemi as the villain's agent.

The problem is that L.A. is already like this. Michael Jackson is
already scarier than the evil Surgeon-General of Beverly Hills. The
knife-wielding punks are less frightening than Johnny Rotten and
the Sex Pistols' senior tour. And what was Judge Ito's courtroom
but a gladiatorial sports arena?

Rob and I walked out of the theater sorely disappointed. "We
could do better than that," Rob said. "I mean, what's it really
going to be like in L.A. in the year 2013?"

We sat for the next half-hour at an outdoor café table, concocting our own L.A. dystopia:

In 2013, it will take more than a tattoo and a nose ring to look
like a bad boy: the new craze will be silicon horns implanted in
the forehead, or better yet, male members harvested from garden-
variety transsexuals. Also popular are articulated tails capable of
wielding weapons or steering vehicles, and all-over repigmentation
jobs in paisley, 3-D Escher prints, or zebra stripes. Steroid-based
drugs that make people grow fur are rejected as being too hot for
the climate, but do manage to become the first recorded Canadian
style statement.

In 2013, traditional aesthetic surgery will be outdated. Instead, most middle-class parents will attach special craniofacial training helmets to the heads of infants, so that the adult facial features are molded to resemble those of Famous Figures in History and Popular Culture. In the year 2013 alone, 170,000 retrochic Jerry Garcia refeaturing kits are sold at Target stores in the Valley, though John Tesh remains the best-selling imago of all time.

In 2013, there will be a resurgence of interest in hunter-gatherer religious traditions, including the notion that you are what you eat—i.e., that people take on the qualities of the animals whose flesh they consume. Naturally, there will be a sharp decline in the popularity of cow and chicken flesh, and the jaguar farms of Bakersfield will become the country's new badlands.

In 2013, the only legal construction material will be Styrofoam, praised for its versatility, insulating qualities, and earthquake safety. In 2013, Kaufman & Broad, in partnership with the McDisney conglomerate, will introduce the first planned Styrofoam community on the former site of UCLA, with a ribbon-cutting ceremony presided over by Mayor Robert Downey, Jr.

In 2013, movie studios will double as correctional facilities, the punishment for any serious crime being servitude in the film business, a limited-access edifice whose anarchistic hierarchy is based on careful anthropological studies of the social structures of the late-twentieth-century federal penitentiary. Actual stardom is, of course, reserved as punishment for the worst offenders.

Satisfied that we'd come up with a Los Angeles scarier than the one we already know, Rob and I sucked the last drop from our Frappuccinos and departed Citiwalk for our Hollywood lowland homes. On the way down the hill, we passed an Angelyne billboard, looked at each other, and shrugged. It was suddenly clear that the whole idea of applying the precepts of science fiction to Los Angeles was patently ridiculous: when you live in a place that prides itself on brinksmanship, the whole point is that it is always worse or better or more or less than anything else you can think of. It's the very essence of a frontier town, which is what Los

Angeles is, for better or for worse, and will be until we colonize Mars.

There may yet be a way to escape from New York—or the Valley of the Dolls, or the Center of the Earth, or the Island of Dr. Moreau, or even Celebration, Florida—but there is no escape from L.A.

NAKED
David Sedaris

'Sidesplitting . . . Not one of the essays in this new collection failed to crack me up; frequently I was helpless'   *New York Times*

From the author of BARREL FEVER, a humorist whose 'satirical brazenness holds up next to Twain and Nathanael West' (*New Yorker*), comes this new collection, in which he hitchhikes across the country with a bizarre collection of quadriplegics and deadbeats who don't always take him where he wants to go; contemplates the fine distinctions between fancy and extra-fancy as he toils as a migrant fruit-picker; celebrates Christmas at the Sedaris residence with friends, family and a recently paroled prostitute; and packs his socks and suntan lotion for a visit to a nudist colony.

Above all, he reintroduces us to one of the great mothers of literature: 'I don't know how it happened, but you're mine. If that's a big disappointment for you, just imagine what I must feel.'

'David Sedaris recreates the cathartic, the spiritual experience of laughing so hard it hurts . . . NAKED is sharp, sympathetic and wonderfully written'   Francine Prose, *New York Observer*

'From cavorting at a nudist colony known for its "pudding toss", to playing fancy-fruit picker in Oregon, David Sedaris lets it all hang out'   *Vanity Fair*

£7.99   0 575 40140 0

INDIGO

TEN WOMEN WHO SHOOK THE WORLD

Sylvia Brownrigg

'Funny, clever and extremely idiosyncratic, the product of a new imagination'

Charles Saumarez Smith, 'Books of the Year', *Observer*

'Her imagination is notably inventive and untrammelled . . . a writer with a sophisticated and elegant feeling for words who is able to run far with the myriad potentialities of language'

Elizabeth Young, *Guardian*

' . . . a true original'

Elaine Feinstein, *The Times*

' . . . not only succeeds in melding the weird with the mundane, but does so with heart, intelligence and great humour . . . I'm sure most people who read TEN WOMEN will re-read it . . . '

Mat Coward, *Tribune*

' . . . good-natured, often joyous, and in the best sense sweet . . . One wants more of these sexy, wild achievers'

Adrianne Blue, *Independent*

£5.99   0 575 40150 8

*IND*I*GO*

Out of the blue . . .

*IN*D*IGO*

the best in modern writing

NON-FICTION

Nicholas Jones *Soundbites and Spin Doctors*	£8.99	0 575 40052 8
David Owen *Balkan Odyssey*	£8.99	0 575 40029 3
Peter Hennessy *The Hidden Wiring*	£7.99	0 575 40058 7
Elizabeth Jenkins *Jane Austen*	£7.99	0 575 40057 9
Jessica Mitford *Hons and Rebels*	£6.99	0 575 40004 8
Louis Heren *Growing Up Poor in London*	£6.99	0 575 40041 2
Stuart Nicholson *Ella Fitzgerald*	£6.99	0 575 40032 3
Nick Hornby *Fever Pitch*	£5.99	0 575 40015 3
Victor Lewis-Smith *Inside the Magic Rectangle*	£6.99	0 575 40014 5
Jim Rose *Freak Like Me*	£6.99	0 575 40033 1
Stephen Burgen *Your Mother's Tongue*	£6.99	0 575 40090 0
Simone de Beauvoir *America Day by Day*	£7.99	0 575 40160 5
Nicola Baird *The Estate We're In*	£6.99	0 575 40156 7
Robert Twigger *Angry White Pyjamas*	£6.99	0 575 40124 9
Birute M F Galdikas *Reflections of Eden*	£7.99	0 575 40002 1
Arno Karlen *Plague's Progress*	£6.99	0 575 40012 9

*IN*D*IGO* books are available from all good bookshops or from:

> Cassell C.S.
> Book Service By Post
> PO Box 29, Douglas I-O-M
> IM99 1BQ
> telephone: 01624 675137, fax: 01624 670923

While every effort is made to keep prices steady, it is sometimes necessary to increase prices at short notice. Cassell plc reserves the right to show on covers and charge new retail prices which may differ from those advertised in the text or elsewhere.